All Our Lives:
A Women's Songbook

Diana Press

Baltimore, Maryland

Library of Congress Cataloging in Publication Data
Main entry under title:

All our lives.

    Unacc., with guitar symbols.
    Bibliography: p.
    1. Women--Songs and music. 2. Music, Popular (Songs, etc.)--United States. I. Cheney, Joyce, 1950-
II. Deihl, Marcia, 1949-   III. Silverstein, Deborah, 1949-
M1977.W64A4 [M1630.18] 784.6'8'301412 76-22564
ISBN 0-88447-008-3

Cover photographs:

New Harmony Sisterhood Band
Photograph by Michael Macy

Photograph Courtesy Robert Gear

Almeda Riddle
Photograph by Suzanne Szasz

Photograph by Jane Melnick

Holly Near
Photograph by Barbara Gundle

Front and back cover design by Jane Simon.

Book design and layout by Joyce Cheney and Deborah Silverstein.

Introduction primarily written by Marcia Deihl.

Notes drawn by Joyce Cheney.

Typeset, printed and bound by Diana Press, Inc.

All Our Lives:
A Women's Songbook

EDITED BY
JOYCE CHENEY , MARCIA DEIHL, AND DEBORAH SILVERSTEIN

We'd like to dedicate this book to the continuing
growth and strength of the women's movement and to
all people's liberation struggles around the world.

Acknowledgements

There are many people we wish to thank for help and inspiration and we will list as many as we can call to mind. Most of the ideas which spawned this folk music approach were gathered in the Cambridge Goddard Graduate School for Social Change's "Forms of Female Expression--Music" project. The instigator of the course, Lanayre Liggera, is perhaps most responsible for carving out the existence of the project. Others taking part in the discussions over the year were Katie Tolles, Marian Leighton, Dusty Miller as well as Deborah Silverstein and Marcia Deihl. Without Rounder Records, the tremendous wealth of songs could not have been gathered. The existence of the New Harmony Sisterhood Band was an invaluable testing ground for these songs--thanks to Lanayre, Deborah, Marcia, Katie, Kendall Hale and Pat Ouelette. Other people who helped point us in the direction of songs were Nancy Ackerman, Florence Brunnings, Ellen Shumsky, Carol Levin, Lorraine Lee, Ruth Pettis, Jan Downey, Ted Warmbrand, The Red Basement Singers, Debby McClatchy, Charlotte Taft, Patty Larkin, Margaret MacArthur, Barbara Carns, Angie Sherbo, Jane Simon, and many others. Moral and spiritual support were provided all along by the women at New Words Bookstore, Karen Lindsey, Sylvia Stein (who helped proofread and publisher-hunt), the Boston Women's Music Collective, and Dorothy Dean of *Paid My Dues*. And thanks for the help and moral support from Judy Gelfand, Carol Cheney and the Bozo Redbird family.

Table of Contents

Introduction

This is a songbook about women--many different kinds of women: women of the past, present and future. We have included these songs (with both negative and positive images of women) because they reflect the transition in our own lives and in the lives of women who struggled before us. As women and as feminists who love folk music and who love to sing, we have produced this book as a reflection of our own struggles in a society which still has so little room for a woman with a mind of her own--even less room for a woman with a song of her own.

There are songs of pain that sing out the feelings of despair with a world whose purpose is to keep women in their place--down. There are songs that reflect our awakening consciousness of our relation to the world around us, politically and economically. There are songs of love, that sing out the joy of women loving women.

Collecting songs for this book was pretty easy; selecting the songs was difficult, especially in the contemporary section. Conscious feminist music began appearing around the late 1960's along with the "second wave" of the women's movement in this country. There was the album *Mountain Moving Day* by the New Haven Women's Liberation Rock Band and the Chicago Women's Liberation Rock Band, which was the inspiration for many women who wanted to combine music and feminism. In the January/February 1971 issue of *Sing Out!*, the folksong magazine, most of the magazine was devoted to women, and a later issue in 1972 included coverage of women's workshops at folk festivals around the country. *Folk Scene*, a west coast folk magazine, published a women's issue with interviews with the more prominent stars of the folk scene. Jerry Silverman attempted the first comprehensive collection of old and new women's songs (though none were recently composed feminist songs). A collection of contemporary feminist songs came out of the Women's History Research Library in Berkeley, California. In Febraury of 1974, *Paid My Dues*, "the first and only feminist journal of women and music", made its appearance as a national forum for women's music. In late May/early June of 1974, there was a National Women's Music Festival in Champaign-Urbana, Illinois.

Although none of the "big name" performers appeared (the booking agent never followed through and not-so-mysteriously disappeared during the festival), and the concert promoters are still bailing themselves out of debt by selling tapes, T-shirts, and chocolate cookies, the event will go down in the women's music annals as a great success. The women who did show up got together and shared as audience and performers, and the absence of the stars was eventually viewed as the best thing that could have happened. The festival was repeated the next year, with many different groups and individuals participating. And by this time, many cities had been organizing their *own* women's music festivals--not only that, but spreading the word that it was possible for any sufficiently dedicated group of women to take their own culture into their own hands (see "Producing Concerts" available from Woman's Soul Publishing). The problem with covering all of the women's music happening as of the fall of 1975 is (wonderfully) that there is too much of it! In Boston, in October of 1975, women from all over the country committed to a conscious women's music performed for three nights in a row--leading many to comment that it was like a feminist Woodstock. And after a short breather, a local Boston festival followed in November, with workshops aimed at incorporating more and more of the listeners with the music-makers in hopes of making women's culture a participatory event as well as an entertainment.

Along with the increase in concert production, there has been the need for crystallization of the sound--in the form of records. Olivia Records is a woman-owned and operated record company which is a precious resource for fans of women's music. Other women have produced their own records and tapes. And with this blossoming of women's music, there is a serious attempt to analyze exactly what it is and how we can perfect and gain from it. There is an up-to-date listing and valuable analysis in the 1975 *The New Woman's Survival Sourcebook* (Knopf) compiled by Susan Rennie and Kirsten Grimstad--turn to page 177 and feast your eyes: women's music has arrived!

The Olivia Record Collective. For information on how to order from Olivia, see no. **70** of the resource list.

The number of women writing songs and publishing their own collections today is astounding. Since our radical messages are not yet acceptable as grist for the mass media mill (if indeed they ever will be, until we are in control!), most of the women we reached were contacted by word-of-mouth or by letters printed in small publications. We have more songs by women in the Boston area than in any other single place because Boston has been our home base. But women around the country are putting their thoughts and feelings into songs about themselves, about all of us, and about the enormous changes that are happening in our lives. This is a songbook about Revolution, for, as we all know, it's Revolution that makes the world go 'round!

Demystification, or How this Songbook Came To Be

At an International Women's Day rally in March of 1974, we met each other for the first time. Joyce was visiting from Vermont, and Marcia and Deborah were playing feminist music for the occasion as part of the New Harmony Sisterhood Band. All of us sensed a need for more feminist music, and we decided to work together to relieve that particular itch by putting out a songbook of the best old and new songs of interest to women. Marica and Deborah had access to many old and contemporary songs through their connection with Rounder Records in Somerville, and Joyce had had experience in trying to publish a book of Vermont folk songs.

There was pooling of fantasies--the excitement and support of sharing a project. Letters and tapes and songsheets went back and forth. Lots of ironing out to do--in blitzes of long-distance weekends in Vermont or Massachusetts. What songs, what format, what rationale, what sort of information to include, what sort of audience to aim at, what publishers to approach? There was some working out among the three of us, strangers working together and getting along. But there is some truth to saying that three people working together produce more than three people would produce separately. We often disagreed and ended up with a product which incorporates two or three viewpoints, perhaps for the better. We helped each other over the hard spots and tried to share work without total specialization.

By June things had shaped up considerably. We had a list of about 70 songs we agreed upon, assignments of researching each song, and categories for organization. We'd written to many music and women's publications for coverage, so that we would reach that unknown woman who had six great original feminist songs in her desk drawer.

Some funny things happened. Like the time Marcia and Deborah found "Bessie Belle and Mary Gray," a song in an old Scottish dialect about two women who had lived together and were buried together out of the graveyard by themselves, "to biek forement the sin." Their "sin", we thought, must have been lesbianism, and we thought we had unearthed a traditional lesbian ballad. After a bit more research, it turned out that they were buried together because they had died of the plague, and "to biek forement the sin" meant "to bake against the sun." Still, "Bessie Belle and Mary Gray" (child ballad No. 201) is a nice song about two women.

Or the time Joyce had gone to tape someone's record of Irish songs for women. It turned out to be a collection of the same old thing--maids waiting on the shore, lamenting for their lovers, and the like. A woman who worked at the record studio came in and said, "These women's songs are all the same. We need some new ones!" A timely bit of encouragement!

This songbook has definitely come together in a traditional female style--the part-time way--through the back door. We squeezed it in between other jobs and commitments. We didn't start at point zero on the "likely-to-succeed" scale, but we were down low there somewhere. We were strangers, living in two different states. We all had other jobs and commitments. We had not enough knowledge and a low budget. We all had in common the frustrating situation of trying to integrate our two main interests--music and feminism. But we did have interest and *motivation from the gut.*

If we didn't know something, we'd ask someone who might, and after two or three referrals, we'd usually find out what we wanted. In some spheres, we had to learn lots before we could know enough to ask the right questions. We had to learn about folklore and the history of women and of music, as well as about technical areas such as copyright rules for printed and recorded songs, copyrights on pictures and illustrations, layout and printing procedures, finances, and how to approach publishers. And on top of all this we were three people diverse in geography, working style, knowledge and available time!

The point of all this is that it *is* possible. Fantasy did become reality. The songs are here, and there can be a sequel if you send your songs and questions too. And as for demystifying your project, it is always hardest to do something the first time. But it no longer is necessary to let fantasies go by. It was true enough, the warning that we got from a friend: Figure out how many hours you think it will take to do it all, then multiply by two. We women cannot afford to fall into the trap of inactivity because we are boggled by the enormities of starting a project. Barriers that kept us from achieving before--no role models, no so-cial reinforcements, skepticism, no money, no childcare--must be overcome. Seize the knowledge you need to do what you want to do. Try to go to other women for help. Set your sights high. We women speak to other women. We touch each others' lives and each other. We enjoy communicating and need to hear from one another.

Why a Women's Culture?

Women's art--literature, theater, painting, dance and music--is just now coming into its own. Culture was defined once in an article by the Chicago Women's Liberation Rock Band as everything that is *not* power or the means of production. That leaves the way we live our lives as well as the arts which we pro-duce. But in some ways, culture is power; it is a subtle form of power in that it provides images and language that shapes our ideas. And those who control our culture, as well as those who control our jobs, create many of the ideas we hold about ourselves as women. In almost all cases, the culture-controllers have been men who have seen women as objects. The phrase "women as objects" may have become trite

Photograph by Bettye Lane

9

by now, but the word "object" typifies what woman's place in the arts has traditionally been: one acted upon, one observed and commented upon, but not one *acting* as a *subject*. At least, not one acting in anything but an acceptably pleasing way.

Breaking the Silence

If nothing seems amiss, there is no wish for change. If someone else defines you, you cannot hope to attain the self-consciousness necessary for liberation. The importance of self-consciousness, of naming the world and creating "new words" as Mary Daly puts it, has been realized by countless women in aptly-named C-R (consciousness-raising) groups. The moment-in-time of realization is as definite as a lightbulb flash, and it keeps recurring--the moment in which women see an old situation in their own terms. As Paolo Friere states it (in non-feminist terms):

That which had existed objectively but had not been perceived in its deeper implications (if indeed it was perceived at all) begins to "stand out", assuming the character of a problem and therefore of challenge. Thus, men begin to single out elements from their "background awareness" and to reflect upon them . . . they come to see the world not as a static reality but as a reality in process, in transformation.[1]

And the step after "seeing" is "breaking the silence." As Sheila Rowbotham puts it,

The oppressed without hope are mysteriously quiet. When the conception of change is beyond the limits of the possible, there are no words to articulate discontent so it is sometimes held not to exist. This mistaken belief arises because we can only grasp silence in the moment in which it is breaking. The sound of silence breaking makes us understand what we could not hear before.[2]

Suni Paz

10

Photograph by Peter Huber

Women's culture is at that breaking point. We are just now able to comprehend that songs express a point of view that is not our own. The silence of alternative images kept us in the roles which we *did* hear about. But with the growth of a self-conscious sexual politics, in addition to the class-conscious politics provided by the Old Left, the latest women's movement brought out protest in the cultural as well as the economic sphere. We want to create a women's culture. Just as with the recent interest by Black people in Black culture and Black Studies, we feel that our history has been distorted and hidden, and that we are still not sure of who we really are or can be, by our *own definition*.

Views of Women Artists

The general feeling about women and creativity is as follows: Men create culture, women create children, and women who seriously try to create anything other than children are deviants who can never be truly fulfilled. Many women who have tried to create have failed because they have tried to make it as a man-in-woman's-clothing, without incorporating a sense of their own female-defined self into their art. Many other women have tried to be both artists and mothers, and couldn't devote full time to either one. It is easier to be a fulfilled father who devotes full time to an art; a father traditionally is not as responsible for being with the children all the time as is a mother. Many women have opted for being semi-proficient at some "serious" art or very good at a craft or folk art which can be picked up and put down (between dishes, diapers, etc.). There seem to be many physical as well as attitudinal handicaps to conquer if a woman is to make it as an artist.

Making It--On Whose Terms?

We want to define ourselves, not just be on the sidelines of the prevailing (male-money-middle class) culture. But what does a women's culture mean? We must try for the merging of what has always been ours and what we wish to keep (the private, personal sphere of the home and loving family) with what has always been denied to us (the public, competitive world of outside evaluation and monetary gain). We must decide which "female" traits we wish to extol and which we wish to throw out. It is too easy to make a virtue of all "womanly" traits, for as Juliet Mitchell says,

> Though "women are wonderful" and "Black is beautiful" are crucial elements in the "dare to struggle, dare to win" stage, they must go hand in hand with a knowledge of what our oppression has done to retard us . . . To say that women have none (or need have none) of the above listed negative feminine characteristics [small-mindedness, petty jealousy, irrational emotionality and random violence, dependence, competitive selfishness and possessiveness, passivity, a lack of vision and conservatism] is moralism, not politics.[3]

If we were to ignore this advice, we would be no better off than the Victorian women who believed "The Cult of True Womanhood"--the idea that women uphold all that is virtuous. In a visionary women's culture we must incorporate what positive virtues we have always had with the power that we have not had. We must try to produce a culture that is more humane, less hierarchical, pluralistic and self-defined.

Taking a practical example, that of the woman artist mentioned above, we can try to imagine what problems would arise in consciously trying to integrate traditional proficiency with feminist quality. A musician playing with a band of other women wants to be as technically proficient as possible. At the same time, women's music groups want to get away from the "star" image of the lead singer or the leader of the band. The traditional male competitive stance would assume that everyone in the band would try to out-do the others in a never-ending grab for recognition. The feminist counterpart, in theory, would be a conscious effort at supporting those who are trying to improve, and in working together for a group result. The glory in such a band is not in the satisfaction of any particular member's ego, but in the feedback and response of the audience to the group as a whole. There is always the problem of criticism—we can't let our efforts go uncriticized and lapse into a technical sloppiness which would render the music useless. But our critics must understand our new aesthetic goals, and temper their criticisms accordingly.

On another level, the performing group wants to relate to the audience in a less oppressive way than male rock musicians. The human function of music, its ability to produce a few moments of transcendence, is a bond between people who play music at all levels, and too often is obliterated by the hard competitiveness of continually striving for technical dominance. For women striving to play fine music, affirmation of commonality of musical impulse between players in a band and between the band and the audience is important. But it isn't enough. Naomi Weisstein has written in *Paid My Dues* (Vol. I, No. 2) about the difficulties and tensions in the Chicago Women's Liberation Rock Band between women who wanted to play with men to better their musical skills, and women who resented or didn't share such drive. The given culture is in the hands of men, and until there are enough women teachers who have the proficiency of male musicians, there is no way we can learn all we need to know from women. But we must make sure our commitments to developing women's culture are equal if we want a group to last--the Chicago one didn't make it.

Although we are eager apprentices in certain technical areas, we wish to *remain* unversed in ruthlessly competitive attitudes. The slickness of sound in a women's band may suffer if all women share in the singing and instrumental importance, but there is a greater chance of all of the musicians reaching their highest potential. In a feminist band, the means to the ends are as important as the end project of a flashy sound.

It is not just a "sour grapes" attitude that determines our separatist nature in relation to prevailing culture. We have chosen to define ourselves, and if we don't measure up to traditional male standards, it's just too bad. How are men to relate to our culture? We can't expect them to be comfortable, for they are eavesdroppers. As Malvina Reynolds, a contemporary songwriter, says in her introduction to a song about abortion called "Rosie Jane":

> This song is addressed to my sisters.
> Any man who is present may listen.

12

Any priest, any public official, any physician.
But it gives him no license to touch us,
We make the decision.[4]

Why A Women's Songbook?

Ancient History

Of all the arts, music is the one which we chose to work with. As a specific form, it goes far back into our history as women. Music itself probably began as chanting by women priestesses in primitive times. The existence of primitive tribes today and the records left of ancient civilizations show that women were in high positions in the spiritual and political life of a community, and their songs and chants were of great importance.

There were rhythmic work songs sung by women working together in the home (a much more conducive atomosphere for group singing then that of the men who were out hunting non-rhythmically and quietly in in the woods!). And on a more public level, the women served as the spiritual guides to the community when they sang songs for birth, marriage and death as well as for successful harvests and battles. All women in the community were actively involved in making music; it was not simply a performing art. With the

Margaret MacArthur

13

coming of christianity and its views of women as sinful temptresses, women were outlawed from singing in the church in 318 A.D. They never regained their position of prominence, and today they play strictly-defined roles in the music world.

What Idiom to Use?

To some extent, all art forms have different idioms--classical, folk and popular. Music has many idioms--blues, soul, folk, classical, jazz, rock, pop--and all of these have a traditional and contemporary component. If we tried to define a women's music in all idioms, it would be an enormous task. Margie Adams, in a June 1974 interview, states that there are aspects of music that surface in all contemporary women's songs that defy categorization into any one idiom. Kay Gardener, who performed on the album *Lavender Jane Loves Women* and whose own album *Mooncircles* has just been released, obviously agrees with Margie on the ideas of a women's instrumental music. She is a classically trained composer who consciously integrates the concepts of non-linear, cyclic musical lines and forms, throbbing rhythmic regularity and ancient modes for arousing various passions, as did the poet Sappha. This affirmation in musical form of the female biological essence is:

> above all, *not* a nostalgic flight away from the pain of reality but rather a journey into awareness of the strength and wholeness in our heritage, which fortifies women for the present and gives impetus to our struggle to regain, come what may, that lost wholeness in our future.
>
> *--Record jacket of Mooncircles*

Although we are consciously creating our present music, the music of the past is broken up into specific genres and women have played differing roles as performers and/or composers in each of them. Classical music scholars have argued through the centuries about the inherent differences in style between women and men composers. In rock and jazz, women have been the exceptions as performers and writers. In pop, soul, folk and blues music, we wail and complain, while pretending to expect no better treatment. No one idiom has superiority as an inherently women's vehicle of expression, but certain aspects of folk music's tradition make it appealing.

Why Folk Music?

By the term "folk" we mean both traditional and contemporary songs, simply accompanied. The technical accessories necessary for most rock, pop and soul arrangements of today make it virtually impossible for women performers to reproduce good music on their own, and they are usually forced into the passive mold of "humming along with the record". These songs should be easy enough for anyone with a guitar to perform and reproduce. They are for people to sing, not for superstars to dub and redub in a studio.

Perhaps because they are simple and unpretentious, they are not widely known. Folk song, both traditional and contemporary, is not the most popular listening fare for most Americans. It exists widely unheard within the prevailing mass-media popular culture. But since it is controllable and reproduceable, it has traditionally been used as an expression of oppressed groups of people from the southern coal miners in the 1930's to the self-consciously folky civil rights supporters in the 1960's.

In a time when traditional singers sang for and about their community (pre-radio 1920's), the music arose from the people it dealt with. Women were especially important as balladeers in their communities and some of them, such as Ola Belle Reed and Almeda Riddle, still sing these songs today. There were no paid stars--performers were good people who had other jobs and sang because they were good at it and enjoyed it. But gradually, some of these country singers encountered technology and promotion. Although radio and records (and now T.V.) brought them a much wider audience, the authenticity and bite of their songs declined. An example of this phenomenon is Elvis Presley's version of "Hound Dog"--a cleaned up version which hit the charts, nothing like the original written by Big Mama Thornton.

If authentic folk songs are unknown and hidden because of the manipulated tastes of the American people, *feminist* folk songs do not fare any better. Most of our musical activity is confined to local performances, radio shows and non mass-media avenues of culture. Our songs serve a community and cannot at this point be successfully transplanted to serve a mass audience without losing their vitality. And we are not very inviting game to a promoter who might be interested in making money off of a statement that a minority of people could relate to.

It is just as difficult for a given woman singer to break into the mass media, if she wishes to retain a feminist identity. Performing music is just that--performing--and that means giving the public what it has been taught to want: honey-throated pristine girls-next-door singing ballads, bluesy wronged or wronging lovers, or back-up choruses going "she-bop she-bop". Women who don't measure up to these conditioned stereotypes aren't going to make it easily on a large scale. We feel a certain security in folk music, for we can reach people in small, comfortable and unadulterated ways.

Feminist Folk Song History

A stab at "sexual politics" was taken as early as 1947 in the American folkie Left. Pete Seeger sang man's-point-of-view songs and Jenny Wells Vincent sang songs where women had the upper hand. They shocked the audience by this breech of "good manners."[6] In 1953, Irwin Silber wrote an article called "Male Supremacy and Folk Song" in *Sing Out!* He deplored the singing of satiric songs aimed at women as part of "attempts to belittle and undermine the role of women in all forms and perpetuate the notion that only men have the capacity to 'run the world'." Without the support of a large women's movement behind him, he later recanted the more dogmatic parts of his article as "masterpieces of inanity, Victorianism, and bigotry."[7]

The original words to "If I Had a Hammer", made popular in the 1960's by Peter, Paul and Mary, were not "sing about the love between my brothers and my sisters" but "sing about the love between all of my brothers." Apparently, the usual problem of the universal use of the word "men" meaning "people" was made more sharp by the use of the word "brothers", which has a distinct gender, and the young singers in People's Artists changed them. But these attempts at consciousness-raising were exceptions.

The Current Folk Scene and Women's Liberation

There is now a raging controversy in the pages of *Sing Out!* over how to handle sexist folk songs. Since folk music and *Sing Out!* in particular have always sided with oppressed groups, this controversy is taken very seriously. In a recent article, Ellen Shumsky wrote:

In my mind the folk scene has always been associated with right causes, people's liberation, protests against injustice, struggles against oppression. I spent lots of summers around the campfire as a child, singing my heart out for the slaves and the workers and the soldiers and the migrants and the organizers . . . Years later, a woman's group reconnected me to myself as a feeling growing organism in a culture that provides little nourishment for the growth of its girl children. I began singing again, but this time I was singing about myself, all women, and I was singing from my gut. This time I was singing my very own song.[8]

She then analyzes the present folk scene in terms of its non-response to the flowering women's consciousness, the satirical and sadistic songs still sung and loved, and the lack of woman-centered consciousness in even supposedly liberated songs.

Her point about singing women's songs of *her own* reminds us of many political statements made by women in the new left groups. They had stopped fighting exclusively for others and were concerned with themselves as women. The class-conscious Old Left had defined songs about workers and poor people as the only truly revolutionary songs; song lyrics were judged solely by their ability to raise class-consciousness. But with the onset of the women's movement, another dynamic, that of sexual politics, has appeared.

We should say "reappeared", for people like Wilhelm Reich had tried to deal with sexual politics in the past and had been put down by orthodox Marxists as concerning themselves with "personal issues." Today the women's movement comes under fire for the same reasons by some sectors of the Left. But more people are coming to see that the revolution involves a wholistic interpretation of life. Politics must expand to include not only where we work but how we live and relate to others. Especially women, who work in the home for no wages and who work in large numbers outside the home at boring and under-paid jobs (which are seen as "pin money" by many employers), need to look at their lives in political terms. We must all see that the "unpaid work" at home is necessary for the continuation of the paid work of commodity production and services. The women's movement is concerned with personal issues because personal issues have always been women's concern. They must be dealt with if women are to achieve psychological as well as economic liberation.

What's a Woman's Song?

This is probably the first question a lot of people might ask. Is any woman singing a song a "women's musician" singing a "women's song"? The mere appearance of a woman singing is in itself a statement that women can be competent musicians and performers. It serves as a role model for women who are considering going into music as a career. Hearing Joan Baez, Bonnie Raitt, Billie Holiday, Janis Joplin, Dory Previn or Peggy Seeger sing and knowing that they are respected as female artists can be one aspect of feminist pride. But apart from the fact that women are performing the music, there is the content of the lyrics to consider. They can range from blatantly shuffling ("...you beat me but I love it" type) to strongly feminist ("We Don't Need the Men"). With the possibility of men writing feminist songs, we have a complex situation involving women singing men's songs, women singing traditionally women's songs, women singing feminist songs, men singing feminist songs . . . aargh! Which are women's songs?

There can be no clear-cut answer. To help our own boggled minds, we have defined Women's Songs as either of two categories: traditional women's songs (those sung about or by women, with particular emphasis on the fact that they are concerned with spheres peculiar to women) and feminist songs (those

Photograph by Mary Alfieri

Holly Tannen (l), Frankie Armstrong, Susie Rothfeld

16

written since the most recent appearance of the women's movement, which raise specifically feminist issues). Traditional women's songs could be lullabies or lamenting love songs, giving us a sense of our past in song. Feminist songs can express self-definition, collective struggles and solutions to women's problems.

Women's music is mostly by women, though not exclusively so. It validates our experience and reinforces experiences that have previously been private. Women's songs give us a sense of our history. They give us new role models. They give us support in the joys and hard times of our changing selves.

In this book we include very few of what, by our own definition, could be called traditional women's songs--those that fit the prevalent stereotypes of women that the patriarchal society holds dear. These songs, whether in the traditional or pop style, paint us as sexy babes and chicks, cheatin' and lyin' bitches, dumb blondes or pure innocents, and little else. We object to the overbearing presence of these songs because they are not just bothersome--they helped form our self-concept as we were growing up and trying to resolve our intrinsic feelings with the images they perpetuated.

Men don't have to define their songs as men's songs, because almost everything that exists in this culture was created by men. And the bulk of songs about women or "by women" are the type that we need not include here--they can be gotten everywhere else. The traditional women's songs which we do include are either unusually positive in their image of women, or else they are particularly illustrative of a historical put-down of women. The feminist songs we include are, needless to say, definitely by and for women.

THE "NEW WORDS": CONTEMPORARY SONGS

The first half of the songbook consists of the contemporary feminist songs. These new songs, or new words, are coming from and contributing to the present women's movement. Although there have been women's "political" songs in the past, such as the suffrage songs which occurred between 1840 and 1918 and the strike support songs of Sarah Ogan Gunning and Aunt Molly Jackson in the 1930's, there has never before been the possibility for feminist songs of such a wide spectrum. As the definition of politics expands to include sexual politics, the definition of a "political" song expands to include songs of love.

There are many lesbian love songs being sung today in women's music circles. Some have been adapted from man-woman love songs by the simple changing of a "he" to a "she", others having been written originally as lesbian love songs. The lesbian community has always suffered at the hands of the heterosexist culture which assumes that all women depend on men for their physical and emotional well-being. In a lesbian relationship, there is an inherent possibility for an easier communication as two equals, not as the male standard and the female other. But is any song about love between two women a lesbian song? Many heterosexuals overlook the fact that *they* are not totally defined as sexual beings, although they are quick to think of homosexuals only in sexual terms. A love song can be about many kinds of love--sexual or platonic, homosexual or heterosexual. Regardless of their sexual preference, women must struggle for their own identities in a male defined culture. Homophobia only obscures our common bonds. Lesbians, by their very existence, undermine the patriarchal myth that "a woman needs a man to be a complete being." Their heterosexual sisters continue to strive for equal relationships with men, and both experiences contribute to a positive women's culture.

As well as songs of support and love, we still sing songs of pain. But instead of repeating that pain is woman's lot, these songs imply that there are ways to stop accepting abuse, and ways to organize as women to become less vulnerable.

And there are songs which deal with women in roles other than those of love-object and love-subject: women as autonomous beings, working and creating. These roles were not traditionally shown in song very often, for these choices have only recently been largely available. Only as the economic and emotional possibility of being independent arose have women been able to break away, and the songs document this current movement. Many women are still not free to be creative beings due to their need to work at stifling jobs for survival, but the possibilities for growth are starting to open. These songs are self-consciously feminist--aimed at change. They reinforce the solidarity that women in the movement feel, and may serve as the first flash of insight for women who have not yet thought much about what the women's movement means for them.

USING THE OLD WORDS: TRADITIONAL SONGS

There are many old ballads and songs which have surprisingly good images of women. But by and large, the songs reflect the historical situation in which women were physically inferior in a frontier situation, where the law of the strong determined the material progress of life. We can't expect songs of the past to contain non-sexist ideas which today we attempt to incorporate into feminist songs. To change the words of a traditional song is to tamper with a story, whether it be one we like to hear or a tale of oppression. So we have included the songs in this section as they first appeared, some terribly sexist and others more progressive. Sometimes we can't even be sure about the "political content" of a song which has undergone many variations ("Who's Gonna Shoe Your Pretty Little Foot").

The themes of traditional stereotyped songs are familiar to us today--we hear the same ones in popular music: women are divided up into pure and impure, those who are sweethearts and mothers and those who are vixens. Although we include some of these songs as examples, many of the songs we include are about women who do not fit pure stereotypes--shrews, witches and adventurers. Some of the less-known songs show women as workers in the factory and in the home, as lovers who aren't putting up with being used, or as political organizers. Part of creating a women's culture is learning from the past. The lyrics of traditional folk songs about women are our history.

When we can look back at ourselves through our own creations, our actions, our ideas, our pamphlets, our organizations, our history, our theory, we begin to integrate a new reality . . . Historical self-consciousness is a tumultous and wayward odyssey which for many of us has only just begun.[9]

CONCLUSION

We have tried to give women's music the public space it must have. We want the music accessible, approachable, understandable, and fun. We have included songs which are all singable--some for more polished musicians, others for rallies and marches. We have included many-versed old ballads which are well worth the time they take to sing, and contemporary to-the-point songs. Look through them, try them, enjoy them!

REFERENCES

[1]Paolo Friere, *Pedagogy of the Oppressed*, Seabury Press, 1974, NYC, p. 70.
[2]Shelia Rowbotham, *Woman's Consciousness, Man's World*, Baltimore, Md.: Penguin, 1973, 1974, p. 29.
[3]Juliet Mitchell, *Woman's Estate*, New York: Vintage, 1973, p. 163.
[4]"Rosie Jane" by Malvina Reynolds, © 1973 by Schroder Music. Used by permission.
[5]See Grace Rubin-Rabson, "Why Haven't Women Become Great Composers", *High Fidelity* (Feb., 1973); George P. Upton, *Woman in Music*, Chicago: A.C. McClury, 1886; Judith Steinberg, "Tuning Out Women Composers", *Women: A Journal of Liberation*, Vol. III, No. 2 (Spring, 1973); Arthur Elson, *Women's Work in Music*, Boston: L.C. Page & Co., 1903; Sophie Drinker, *Women and Music*, New York: Coward & McCann, 1948; and Ashley Montagu, *The Natural Superiority of Women*, New York: Macmillan, 1953, pp. 142-145.
[6]Richard Reuss, *American Folklore and Left-Wing Politics*, 1927-1957, University Microfilm, Ann Arbor, Mich., 1971, p. 339.
[7]Reuss, p. 340.
[8]Ellen Shumsky, "Womansong: Bringing It All Back Home" in *Sing Out!*, Vol. 22, No. 6 (Jan./Feb., 1974) p.9.
[9]Shelia Rowbotham, *Woman's Consciousness, Man's World*, p. 28 .

Contemporary Songs

Escape from Being "The Other"

When some of us first joined C-R groups, we mostly talked about men and our relationships to them. We had never before met to talk exclusively about ourselves as women, as autonomous beings, separate from our men friends, husbands, lovers, fathers and brothers. We exposed some of their tricks and learned to trust in our own feelings, with support from others. "Standing Behind A Man" and "Custom Made Woman Blues" express the wish for women to become full people, not simply exist as appendages to a man. "Talking Want Ad" humorously accomplishes getting across the message that what is expected as a matter of course for women sounds ludicrous when roles are reversed and men are expected to be mere helpmates.

Photograph by Elsa Dorfman

24

Standing Behind A Man

Words and Music by Jane Voss

Jane Voss grew up in Toledo, Ohio and made the 1960's pilgrimmage out to San Francisco. It was around this time that she began to discover traditional American music, especially that of the Carter Family from Virginia which she sings with great style. "Standing Behind A Man" is written in the Carter Family mountain style.

Be- hind ev- ery man who makes a great name, it's said a wo- man does stand,

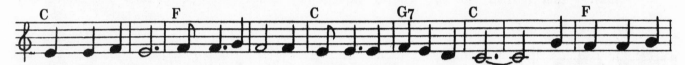

faith- ful and true, will- ing to do, and play an- y part in his plan. Oh, how man-y

lives have been lived out that way, as some- bod- y else's right hand? How man-y

wo-men with- out face- s or names, stand-in' be- hind some man.

2. Once upon a time, I called a man mine,
And I waited at his every whim.
In worry and fear, cried many a tear
In the long nights waiting for him.
Oh, the time that I wasted, the love that I lost,
Measure it nobody can.
I sold my birthright for a warm bed at night
To be standin' behind some man.

3. Now the love of a man is a beautiful thing,
A joy and a comfort so fine.
But if the lovin' you crave just makes you a slave,
You're sellin' yourself down the line.
Each person must have their own work to do,
Each life its own special plan,
And a woman is lost who pays the great cost
To be standin' behind some man.

4. If you take a butterfly by the wing
You know it will never more fly.
If my life must be some small captive thing,
You know that I'd sooner die.
Lovers may come and lovers may go,
But I only have what I am,
And I'd rather be flyin' lonesome and free
Than be standin' behind some man.

You know, I'd rather be flyin' lonesome and free
Than be standing' behind some man.

Source: *Sing Out Magazine*, November/December 1972, p. 19, (85).

Custom Made Woman Blues

Words and Music by Alice Gerrard

Well I tried to be the kind of wo- man you want-ed me to be. And it's not your

fault that I tried to be what I thought you want-ed to see. Smil- in' face and

shin- in' hair, clothes that I thought you'd like me to wear, made to please and

not to tease. It's the cus-tom made wo-man blues.

2. Yes I tried to be the kind of woman you wanted me to be.
And I tried to see life your way and say all the things you'd
Like me to say,
Lovin' thoughts, gentle hands,
All guaranteed to keep ahold of your man,
Made to please and not to tease, it's the
Custom-made woman blues.

3. And now you say you're tired of me
And all those things I thought you wanted me to be,
Is it true you want someone who
Knows how to think and do on her own?
Lord, it's hard to realize, the lessons I learned so young were
Nothin' but lies,
Made to please and not to tease, it's the
Custom-made woman blues.

Source: *Hazel and Alice* LP, Rounder 0027, (45); also (85).

Alice got interested in folk music while she was at Antioch college in Ohio, and has been performing since the early 1960's. Originally from Seattle and California, she now spends most of her time on the east coast and sings with Hazel Dickens (see introduction to "Don't Put Her Down, You Helped Put Her There"). She plays banjo, guitar and autoharp and also sings with The Strange Creek Singers on the Arhoolie and Mercury labels.

She has also written "You Gave Me a Song", written with Hazel in mind, and "Gallop To Kansas" which are both on the Rounder album. Along with Hazel, she has put much time and energy into understanding the roots of traditional folk music, but also expresses herself as a woman today.

Talking Want Ad

Words and Arrangement by Janet Smith

Janet Smith is a professional musician, singer, and songwriter. She has been performing and teaching since high school and ran a folk club in Rome in the late sixties. She plans to have some of her children's songs published and is able and willing to write music, made-to-order.

"Talking Want Ad" presents a radical message in the style of traditional talking blues.

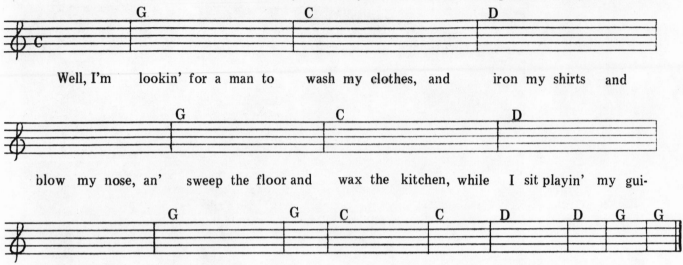

2. Well I'm lookin' for a guy who'll cook my meals
   An' wash my dishes and take the peels
   Off my bananas with a grin
   And ask me how my workday's been . . .
   Terrible as always . . . playin' the guitar is such a struggle!

3. Well I'm lookin' for a guy with curly hair
   And great big muscles and a nice derriere
   Who'll get up nights and feed the baby
   An' bring my coffee when I'm ready . . .
   I gotta feel good in the morning . . .
   That's when I make my best music.

4. So if you feel you'd like to apply
   Why just send a photo or drop on by,
   An' you can shine my shoes today
   An' if you're lucky I'll let you stay
   And cook supper . . . and after you've finished the dishes . . .
   I might even let you stay and listen to me play the guitar!

Source: *Virgo Rising* LP (Thunderbird) (97).

Nuclear Family Blues

Words and Music by Jane Voss

Jane, who brings us "Standing Behind A Man" takes a stab at the nuclear family in this good-natured but all-too-true look at 20th century home life.

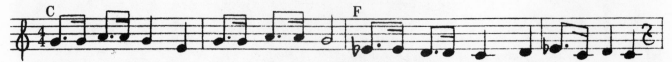

Ba- by's in the cra- dle. Ma- ma's at the sink. Dad- dy's in the back- room try-in' to think;

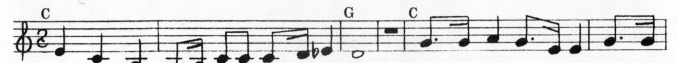

They've got those nu-cle- ar fa- mi- ly blues. Broth-ers and sis- ters all scrap- pin'

in the hall; Lis- ten to the mu- sic, you can hear the kid- dies squall; They've got those

nu-cle- ar fa- mi- ly blues_____. Ma- ma's got 'em. Dad-dy's got 'em. Sis-ter's

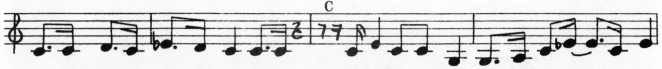

got 'em, and my bro-thers all got 'em, an' I got 'em, those nu-cle- ar fa- mi- ly

blues. You know the Pres-i- dent's got 'em; it's such a sen- sa- tion. That same old blues is

sweep-in' the na- tion. Oh, we got those nu-cle- ar fa- mi- ly blues.

TAG:

You know, we all got those nu- cle- ar fa- mi- ly blues.

2. Daddy's workin' hard, tryin' to bring the bacon home,
   There ain't no relief, he's gotta go it alone;
   He's got those nuclear family blues.
   Just slavin' away the best years of his life,
   Tryin' to make a livin' for his kids and his wife (or "us kids")
   And he's got those nuclear family blues.

3. Now it's every single night around the old TV
   The family gathers, what you get is what you see,
   You get those nuclear family blues.
   The situation comedy and then the commercial,
   Gather 'round children, it's your dress rehearsal,
   You're gonna get those nuclear family blues.

4. All the kids are growin' up and gettin' married outa school,
   A couple of years later, they're playin' the fool;
   They get those nuclear family blues.
   Get married, have a baby, and then the divorce;
   Sister's stuck at home with the baby, of course.
   She gets those nuclear family blues.

5. Well, I went the other night to the movie-picture-show,
   It was Happy Ever After, that's the way it always goes;
   But I got those nuclear family blues.
   That hero started out, he was awful sad and lonely,
   By the movie's end, he had found his One-and-Only,
   But I still got those nuclear family blues.

6. Well, there's a lot o' people talkin' all about we gotta change it,
   But year after year, it's the same old arrangement,
   And we got those nuclear family blues.
   I'm lookin' for some hope for my own generation,
   That same old blues is still sweepin' the nation,
   And we got those nuclear family blues.

7. Well, mama's got 'em, daddy's got 'em,
   Sister's got 'em and my brothers all got 'em,
   An' I got 'em, those nuclear family blues.
   You know the President's got 'em, it's such a sensation,
   That same old blues is sweepin' the nation, oh,
   We got those nuclear family blues.

   Tag: You know we all got those nuclear family blues.

Source: Heard in concert, Boston, 1974.

Darling Annie

Words and Music by Peggy Seeger

"I was born on the 23rd floor of the Flushing Hospital, New York, a first girl to my father after five boys. Needless to say, I was somewhat spoiled. Both my parents were classical musicians. As there were four of us children, both parents worked: my mother taught piano and my father worked at the Pan American Union in Washington. At 7 I took up the piano and during the next twenty years of my life I added the guitar, five-string banjo, concertina, Appalachian dulcimer and autoharp. Education: two years at Radcliffe college and then a twenty year sabbatical to England, which is still in progress. At present, living with Ewan McColl and we have three children. I am enjoying being a housewife because I also help as a singer and musician to earn the living. I work in conjunction with Ewan in doing radio and television programs, music for films, lecturing, and teaching as well as singing in concerts, clubs and festivals. When I am a housewife, I am constantly aware of the problems of a woman stuck in the home, the frustration and the boredom of a type of work which requires chiefly organizational and psychological genius. When I am a 'career woman' I am aware of the pulls of home, the problem of getting time to practice music and learn new songs, aware of how few women artists there are. . ."

Peggy Seeger is a great songwriter. Her songs are true works of art in music and thought. "Darling Annie" challenges the institution of marriage, questioning the outcome of subjecting the delicate balance of a relationship to bureaucracy and the expectations of social roles.

If you mar-ry me, I'll give you ev-ery-thing I have. You will nev-er have to earn a pen-ny——— I will be your man, and the ring up-on your hand will show the world that you're my dar-ling An-nie.

2. Thank you, Love, I'll be glad to add your wages on to mine,
I can work and keep myself so handy;
You can be my man without a golden wedding band.
And I'll tell the world that I'm your Annie.

CHORUS (after every even verse)

For it's love, love will hold us, love is everything
Who could dream of anything that's better?
Not the vow, not the string, not the golden wedding ring,
Just you, Love, you and me together.

3. If you'll marry me, I will give to you my name,
   It will shield you from idle talk and envy,
   For when you play the game, you're secure from any blame,
   Not ashamed to be my darling Annie.

4. Thank you, Love, I'm grateful for the offer of your name,
   But my own will serve as well as any;
   I don't like the game and the rules would make me tame,
   Not the same girl you married, not your Annie.
   CHORUS

5. If you'll marry me, we'll get a house and settle down,
   A place to call your own, so neat and canny;
   With a family and a home, Love, you'll never feel alone,
   Left on the shelf, a spinster, darling Annie.

6. Dearest Love, we could surely find a place to call our own--
   All we need is some influence and money!
   But I don't need a ring, or a house or anything
   To become a mother (or a granny).
   CHORUS

7. If you marry me, I will be faithful unto death,
   You will have all my love and my attention;
   We will care, we will share life in sickness and in health--
   And when I die, you can draw the widow's pension!

8. I will live with you, and I'll be faithful unto death,
   We will share all the burdens we must carry--
   We'll always be free, me for you and you for me--
   And when we're old, Love, maybe we should marry!
   CHORUS

Peggy Seeger

Source: *New City Songster*, No. 7, Jan. 1972 (64).

Malvina Reynolds

34

No Hole in My Head

Words and Music by Malvina Reynolds

Malvina says she wrote this song about censorship--it is still appropriate today, especially if sung by a woman. See the introduction to "We Don't Need the Men" for more about the composer.

Ev- ery bod-y thinks my head's full of no- thin' wants to put his spe- cial stuff in. Fill the space with can- dy wrap- pers, Keep out sex and rev-o- lu- tion but there's no hole in my head, too bad.

2. They call me a dupe of this and the other,
Call me a puppet on a string, they,
They don't know my head's full of me and
That I have my own special thing and there's
No hole in my head, too bad.

3. I have lived since early childhood
Figuring out what's going on, I
Know what hurts, I know what's easy,
When to stand and when to run, and there's
No hole in my head, too bad.

4. So please stop shouting in my ear, there's
Something I want to listen to, there's a
Kind of birdsong up somewhere, there's
Feet walking the way I mean to go and there's
No hole in my head, too bad.

(Repeat first verse)

Source: *Virgo Rising* LP, Thunderbird Records 7037 (97).

(No More) Beggar's Blues

Joanna has moved back to the Boston area from the West, where she produced her own record called "The Greatest Illusion," available through Rounder Records. The record was a reflection of her thoughts concerning friends, spirituality and her sisters especially. She has a powerfully beautiful voice, and has lent her talents to workshops in the area, singing songs such as this one--a much-needed look at the traditional blues as women sang them, and her modern-day response. It is a feminist statement, but also a tribute to the blues women of the past.

Note from Joanna: "I play it fingering Am, Fmaj7 etc. with the capo up 3 or 4 frets, so the chords of the last line go like this, with a nice ascending base run:

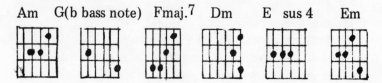

Am   G(b bass note)   Fmaj.7   Dm   E sus 4   Em

As in any blues, work the words loosely and melody more so, slow and strong."

Source: WHRB Open Hoot, Boston, 1975.

(No More) Beggar's Blues

Words and Music by Joanna Cazden

No more time for cry- in', Put- tin' up with pain. No more time for sigh- in', "Oh it's

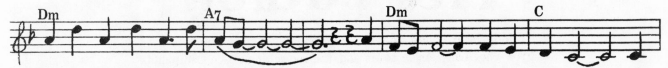

bad but I guess I'm to blame————!" We'll sing of love, we'll sing lone- ly—— we'll

sing out in three's or two's But wo- men got no more wind for beg- gars' blues!

bridge (half-spoken)

Bil- lie, your lov- er- man beat you. Jan- is Pearl, babe, they al- ways cheat you;

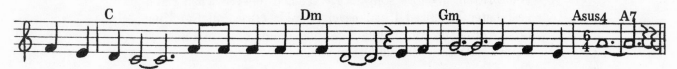

Ma- ma Bes- sie, did- n't they mis- treat you? But no more, sis- ters, no more!

2. Anyone who says it's easy, you know they've never tried
   But the ones who complain so hard never will be satisfied
   We'll carry our share, help out a friend
      But to slave we must refuse
   'Cause women got no more wind for beggars' blues.

   (BRIDGE)

      Billie, that lover man beat you
      Janis Pearl, Babe, they always cheat you
      Mama Bessie, didn't they mistreat you
      but no more, sister, no more!

3. We got no pimp, we got no broker, got no one on the squeeze
   We've just got ourselves and our people to please
   It's a change in the story
      Gonna be a change in the news
   'Cause women got no more wind for beggars' blues!

Free To Grow

Holly Near is best known for her singing contributions to the Free The Army Asian tours and the Indochina Peace Campaign tours. *Hang in There* contains many songs about the Vietnam War, as well as more personal songs. Her second ablum, *Holly Near, A Live Album*, contains more songs of her past as a middle-class U.S. woman growing up. Her latest album *You Can Know All I Am* on Redwood Records features "Flyin'," and "Sister Woman Sister."

In *Sing Out!*, Vol. 22, No. 6 (Jan/Feb, 1974) Holly says:

It's funny, I find myself apologizing to my political audience when I write and sing a love song, full of my weaknesses. And I find myself apologizing to my conservative and liberal audiences for having ruined their day with a political song. I recall one man saying, "You have a pretty voice and I like some of the music, but isn't it a little redundant? All those 'protest songs'? Haven't you written any love songs?" He seemed relieved when I said yes. Later I realized I had never heard a critic call Nat King Cole redundant for singing a whole album of love songs. Is change not less redundant than love?

Holly Near

Free To Grow

Words and Music by Holly Near

I run in- to you in man-y cit- ies—— We both trav- el of- ten in

our trade. And I won-der what your wo- man feels home a- lone,

tak- ing care of child- ren and mind- ing your home. Oh I've nev-er found a man

who would do it for me———— Nev-er found a man who said he could wait

while I was free——— to go, free to grow ———. And. I ———.

Though my work will take me round the coun- try, I don't think I'll ev- er

wan-na have the right to make a- noth- er feel that he or she

must give up liv- ing while I grow. It seems so wrong to- day but I just want

40

to know what you say to make her stay. It must be some-thing in your man-ly

way that keeps her down. Oh I've (to chorus)

3. 2nd ending - chorus

go I wan-na be free to grow, free to grow.

(fine)

2. And I wonder what you tell her when she's lonely,
To pacify her for another day,
Does she put the kids to bed,
Then read or watch T.V.
While you're out being someone
That you want to be?

Source: *Holly Near: A Live Album* LP, Redwood Records (A).

Working Class Woman

Words by Barbara Dane, Adapted From Original Lyrics by Jane Felczer and Peter Boyd
Music by Kendall Hale

Jane Felczer wrote a song based on the struggles she was experiencing in her own life. Barbara Dane re-wrote the song from the perspective of a working class woman who is beginning to view her problems within the context of her developing class consciousness.

Please note that the musical arrangement in this book is entirely different from the one on the album. The song is very powerful in either style.

Barbara Dane has sung songs of struggle for years, and recently produced and sang on the album, *I Hate the Capitalist System* for Paredon Records. She has worked for 10-15 years in "commercial pastures" and has devoted much time to singing about women's lives and times through the blues medium.

Joe work-ing-man's wife, that's how I was de-fined, as if that was my life. my
And in time there were ba- bies had to make us a home. Joe was work- ing two jobs, I was

hope and my mind. But I worked in a bake-shop, did the house- work at night.
al- ways a- lone. I need- ed some time and just a lit- tle con- trol

There was no time to stop for a young bird in flight. I want- ed a
just to keep my right mind, just to try to stay whole.

part- ner to be his friend not just his wife. I'll work hard for my child- ren, but

they're my love, not my life. And I know it takes lov- ing and I know it takes

time, but I'm a work- ing class wo- man and the fu-ture is mine.

fu- ture is mine ————.

3. Went to work in a factory, and
   it's rough in this world.
   My kids are in high school, and
   the boss calls me 'girl",
   But on the woman beside me, as we sweat
   on the line
   Says, "Tommorow is payday, and the
   next day is mine.!"

4. It's a race for the strong, 'cause it'll
   grind up the meek,
   When your money runs short, at the
   end of the week.
   And your car needs some tire,
   And your kids need some shoes.
   For a working class woman
   That's an old kind of blues.

CHORUS 2
This system buys hands, but you
   must not use your head,
It'll shake you and break you, 'til
   all your senses are dead.
And I know it takes lovin',
   And I know it takes time,
But I'm a working class woman,
   And the future is mine.
I'm a working class woman,
   And the future is mine.

5. But I know there are answers,
   I gotta get to the source.
   I think me and this system gotta
   get a divorce.
   I can't make enough money, I can't
   find enough time,
   But I'm a working class woman, and
   the future is mine.

6. Well, there's more where I come from,
   and we got anger to burn.
   And we're talkin' and movin', gonna
   study and learn.
   Build a unity train, on a straight-
   arrow line.
   If today is the bosses', I know
   tomorrow is mine.

CHORUS 3
I wanted a partner, to be his friend
   not just his wife,.
I'll work hard for my children
   but they're my love not my life.
And I know it takes lovin',
   And I know it takes time,
But I'm a working class woman,
   And the future is mine.
I'm a working class woman,
   And the future is mine.

Source: *I Hate the Capitalist System* LP, Paredon P-1014 (51).

Ramblin' Woman

Words and Music by Hazel Dickens

Here is a more recent song by Hazel Dickens (see "Don't Put Her Down You Helped Put Her There" for more information on Hazel) which speaks to the ideas of a new woman--one which still shocks many traditional supporters of the elusive "dream cottage built for two."

You been hand-in' me a lot of sweet talk 'bout things you want us to do. Said you're think-ing a-bout sett-lin' down in a dream-house built for two. Well I hate to dis-ap-point you, but I don't fit in-to that plan, 'cause I'm a ram-blin' wo-man, and you're a home love-in' man. Yes, I'm a ram-blin' wo-man, and I hope you'll un-der-stand, 'cause you know a ram-blin' wo-man's no good for a home lov-in' man.

44

2. Yes, there's a whole lot of places
   My eyes are longin' to see,
   Where there is no dream cottage,
   No babies on my knee.
   And there's a whole lot of people
   Just waitin' to shake my hand.
   And you know a ramblin' woman's
   No good for a home—lovin' man.

3. So take all of that sweet talk
   And give it to some other girl
   Who'd be happy to rock your babies,
   And to live in your kind of world.
   But I'm a different kind of woman,
   With a different set of plans.
   And you know a ramblin' woman's
   No good for a home—lovin' man.

Photograph by Jane Melnick

Source: Heard in concert, Boston, 1974.

Fantasy Girl

Words and Music by Alix Dobkin

Alix Dobkin and Kay Gardner are competent and polished musical performers. It feels good to have them as spokeswomen for us through their music. Not only are they competent, but it shines through that they believe in and find joy in their music.

This song is more in the performing pop genre than many folk songs in this book. A slap in the face--or laugh in the face--to men, telling them to wake up and see what we think of the deals they've offered us, what we think of how they see us, and telling them we've changed.

See the introduction to "A Woman's Love" for more about Alix and Kay.

46

She's a great big throw a- way girl, e- lu- sive, un- ob- tru- sive ba- by and

She's a ti- ny ten- der tin- der- box, she rolls her eyes, she walks she talks, she's wait-in'

for you, Boop boop bee doo, well fi-nal- ly the times have changed, your sug- ar ba- by's

re-ar- ranged, so watch it boy when you ca- ress, that pus- sy is a li- on- ess woo——

She's a Boy, does she know you. She's seen right through the Boop boop bee doo.

Source: *Lavender Jane Loves Women* LP, Women's Wax Works, A001 (58).

No Deposit, No Return

Words and Music by Anne Romain

Anne Romaine has been active in community struggles in the South for many years. She is perhaps best known for organizing the Southern Folk Tour for the past eight years, a concert tour which has featured Hazel and Alice, Bessie Jones and many other performers. She has studied singing with Bernice Reagon of Sweet Honey in the Rock and has recently moved to Nashville.

This song is a complaint song, but with the crucial ingredient for the woman who wants to put her foot down--a demand for change. This is quite the opposite of the many country songs in which the "lucky" woman finally wins back her wandering man with grateful arms. Other songs on the album include a song about Joan Little, "On the Line", "Georgia Cotton Mill Woman", 'Indiana Factory Job" and her own version of Beverly Grant's "Gettin' On Woman."

Now you're beg-gin' me to take you back and for- get our yes- ter- days——

You prom-ised me you've giv- en up your dis- ap- pear- in' low- down

ways—— But you're a sweet-talk-in' man used to get- tin' your way and you've

al- ways had that way with words, but I ain't tak-in' you back on

words this time, no de- pos- it, no re- turn. No de- pos- it, no re- turn,

I touched you and got burned. You're gon- na get a dose of what I've been through

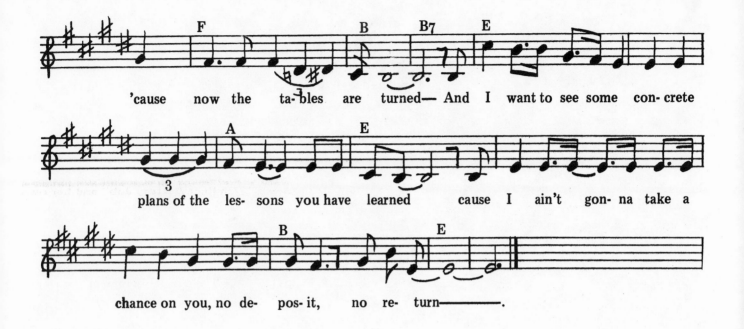

'cause now the ta-bles are turned— And I want to see some con-crete

plans of the les- sons you have learned cause I ain't gon- na take a

chance on you, no de- pos- it, no re- turn————.

2. You know, I always thought you were the very best man
   To ever come down the track.
   This time you better listen hard
   Before you start to unpack.
   'Cause I want to see a change in you,
   Some understanding and a little concern.
   It may seem too much to ask of you, but
   No deposit, no return.

CHORUS 2

   No deposit, no return,
   I touched you and got burned.
   You're gonna get a dose of what I've been through
   'Cause now the tables are turned.
   And I want to see a change in you,
   Some understanding and a little concern,
   'Cause I an't gonna take a chance on you--
   No deposit, no return.

TAG

   'Cause I ain't gonna take a chance on you.
   No deposit, no return.

Source: *Gettin' On Country* LP, Rounder 3009 (B).

Song of My Mother

Helen Tucker is a member of the folksinging trio, Charley's Aunts, which is featured on the album *Virgo Rising*. This song came out of a project on aging which was produced for KQED T.V. in the Bay Area in California. Copies of a booklet about the project may be obtained from: Trish Sommers, c/o Women's Action Training Center, 1941 High St., Oakland, California 94601.

Helen Tucker, by the way, is happily celebrating her forty-second birthday this year.

Photograph by Jane Melnick

Mother and daughter

Song of My Mother

Words and Music by Helen Tucker

Some-one said to me to-day, "My dear, you're grow-ing old. I had-n't

real-ized how you aged, I wish that I'd been told. Your cheeks have lost their

mus-cle, all those lines up-on your face. You must be hav-ing trou-ble

keep-ing up with this mad pace!" Well, I said, "I'm for-ty. Did you

ex-pect to see the skin and fig-ure of a wo-man bare-ly past her

teens? Though my cheeks are sag-ging, I've just now reached my prime

Just take an-oth-er look in-to these bright eyes of mine!"

2. Someone said to me today, "My Dear, what do you do?
Since now your children all are gone, what could interest you?
You must be going crazy in that empty house alone
With no one there who needs you--how nice to have a phone."
Well, said I, "I'm fifty, and did you really think

Your children would remain with you, that there'd be no broken link?
Tho' I'm all alone now, I'll tell you what I've found--
A time for me, a life for me--isn't that a joyful sound?"

3. Someone said to me today, "My Dear, what do you eat?
You mustn't have much money--look at the shoes upon your feet.
Do your children help you? You're much too old to hire.
I'm sure the young girls get the jobs, for you would surely tire."
Well, said I, "I'm sixty, and I truly wish you knew
Of all the wisdom that I have from the years that I've been through.
For I have not been stagnant and I've learned what I can do.
It's time that others realized I need to work for money too."

4. Someone said to me today, "I see you're still alone.
How lonely it must be to·have no man to call your own.
But then I guess you've reached that age when love can't mean that much.
How sad 'twould be to think that you still hungered for that touch.
Well, said I, "I'm seventy, and tho' my bones have set,
Don't think that I don't have a little loving in me yet!
Though I do quite well alone, I still have lots to give,
And I still find my greatest joy in sharing what I live."

Photograph by Elsa Dorfman

Source: *Paid My Dues*, Vol. I, No. 2, p. 9 (73).

"You Helped Put Her There"

Sure, Women often do silly and petty things. But instead of accepting such traits as natural vices of womankind, we must understand that we have been molded and forced into certain ways of acting, and that it is often the men who criticize us who expect us to act in stereotyped ways. "Don't Put Her Down You Helped Put Her There" states it beautifully. "It Wasn't God Who Made Honky Tonk Angels" and "Just Because I'm A Woman" (see reference list no. 19) aren't really consciously-written feminist songs, but they state pretty clearly the woman's side of the situation, as do many country-western lyrics. A few lines from "I'm Gonna Be An Engineer" (see p. 64) sum up the problems of sex stereotyping:

> You got one fault, you're a woman,
> Not worth the equal pay,
> Bitch or a tart, you're nothing but heart,
> Shallow and vain, you got no brain,
> You even go down the drain like a lady today. [1]

The ways in which society sees us aren't just inconvenient--they are responsible in part for the low wages which keep us in a dependent role.

[1]"I'm Gonna Be An Engineer" by Peggy Seeger, © 1971 by Shelter Music. Used by Permission.

Photograph from *Vermont Album—A Collection of Vermont Photographs*, edited by Ralph Nading Hill, copyright © 1974, Steven Greene Press. Used by permisision. Courtesy Vermont Historical Society.

Don't Put Her Down

Hazel was born and raised in the coal camps of West Virginia and followed eleven brothers and sisters to Baltimore, Maryland in search of something better. She met Alice Gerrard in the Washington, D.C.-Baltimore area, and was encouraged to sing the songs that she had grown up with. Since then, she and Alice have sung together as a women's country and bluegrass duo (no mean feat for the bluegrass idiom!) on Rounder, Folkways and Verve-Folkways labels. The two women also perform with the Strange Creek Singers on the Arhoolie and Mercury labels, singing traditional and contemporary topical and mining songs.

Hazel plays guitar and bass, and is an enormously talented songwriter, as more and more people in the folk world are beginning to realize. Some of her other songs are "Pretty Bird" and "My Better Years", both on the "Hazel and Alice" record, and she is still writing. The feminist statements of Hazel and Alice have penetrated the country music scene, where they are much needed. Both women are committed to mastering the tradition from which their songs come, but are equally committed to expressing themselves as contemporary women.

Photograph by Jane Simon

Hazel Dickens (L) and Alice Gerrard (R)

Source: *Hazel and Alice* LP, Rounder 0027 (45).

Don't Put Her Down

Words and Music by Hazel Dickens

You pull the string. She's your play- thing. You can make her or break her it's true. You a- buse her, ac- cuse her, turn a- round and use her, and for- sake her an- y time it suits you. Well there's more to her than pow- der and paint, and her per- ox- id ed bleached out hair. Well if she acts that way it's 'cause you've had your day. Don't put her down - you helped put her there.

2. She hangs around playin' the clown
While her soul is achin' inside,
Well, she's heartbreak's child cause she just lives for your smile
To build her up in a world made by men.

CHORUS

3. At the house down the way
You sneak and you pay
For her love, her body or her shame,
Then you call yourself a man, say that you just don't understand
How a woman could turn out that way.

Well there's more to her than powder and paint
And the men she picks up at the bar,
Well if she acts that way it's 'cause you've had your day,
Don't put her down, you helped put her there.

It Wasn't God Who Made Honky Tonk Angels

Words and Music by J.D. Miller

Hank Thompson wrote a country western hit called "The Wild Side of Life," the story of an "evil" woman who left behind the proper life of home and family. Kitty Wells recorded "It Wasn't God Who Made Honky Tonk Angels" in 1953 as a direct response to Thompson's damnation of "honky tonk" women "Honky Tonk Angels" became the first major country western hit sung by a woman. SOMEBODY out there was listening!

2. Now it's a shame that all the blame is on us women,
It's not true that only you men feel the same.
'Cause from the start 'most every heart that's ever broken
Always was because there was a man to blame.

CHORUS

Source: *Frank Wakefield with Country Cooking* LP, Rounder 0007 (40).

I'm Gonna Be An Engineer

Words and Music by Peggy Seeger

"I'm Gonna Be An Engineer" has to be the all time epic ballad of the Women's Movement. You wouldn't think a song so long could be so interesting, but Peggy's story of a woman's life-long struggle to fulfill her desires covers issues from anti-tomboyism to equal pay for equal work.

When I was a lit-tle girl I wished I was a boy. I tagged a- long be- hind the gang and

wore me cor-du- roys. Ev- ery bod- y thought I on-ly did it to an- noy, but I was

gon-na be an en-gin- eer! Mam- ma told me, "Can't you be a la- dy? Your

du-ty is to make me the moth-er of a pearl. Wait un- til you're old- er dear and

may- be you'll be glad that you're a girl." Dain- ty as a Dres-den stat-ue;

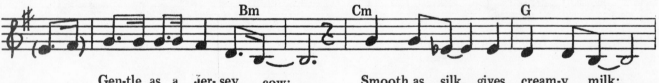

Gen-tle as a Jer-sey cow; Smooth as silk, gives cream-y milk;

Learn to coo; learn to moo; that's what you do to be a la-dy now.

Source: *At This Present Moment* LP, Rounder 4003, (12).

2a When I went to school I learned to write and how to read,
   Some history, geography and home economy,
   And typing is a skill that every girl is sure to need,
   To wile away the extra time until it's time to breed,
   And then they had the nerve to say, 'What would you like to be?"
   I says "I'm gonna be an engineer!"

b "No, you only need to learn to be a lady,
   The duty isn't yours for to try and run the world,
   An engineer could never have a baby,
   Remember dear that you're a girl."

3a So I became a typist and I study on the sly,
   Workin' out the day and night so I can qualify,
   And every time the boss came in, he pinched me on the thigh,
   Says, "I've never had an engineer!"

b "You owe it to the job to be a lady,
   It's the duty of the staff for to give the boss a whirl,
   The wages that you get are crummy, maybe,
   But it's all you get 'cause you're a girl."

c She's smart (for a woman),
   Wonder how she got that way?
   You get no choice, you get no voice,
   Just stay mum, pretend you're dumb,
   That's how you come to be a lady today.

4a Then Jimmy came along and we set up a conjugation,
   We were busy every night with lovin' recreation,
   I went back to work so he could get his education,
   And now *he's* an engineer!

b He says, "I know you'll always be a lady,
   It's the duty of my darlin' to love me all my life.
   Could an engineer look after or obey me?
   Remember dear, that you're my wife."

5a As soon as Jimmy got a job I studied hard again,
   Then busy at me turret-lathe a year or so and then
   The morning that the twins were born, Jimmy says to them,
   "Kids, your mother was an engineer."

b "You owe it to the kids to be a lady,
   Dainty as a dishrag, faithful as a chow,
   Stay at home, you got to mind the baby,
   Remember you're a mother now."

6a Everytime I turn around there's something else to do,
   Cook a meal or mend a sock or sweep a floor or two,
   I listen in to Jimmy Young— it makes me want to spew,
   "I was gonna be an engineer!"

b I really wish that I could be a lady,
   I could do the lovely things that a lady's s'posed to do,
   I wouldn't even mind if only they would pay me,
   And I could be a person too.

c What price -- for a woman?
   You can buy her for a ring of gold,
   To love and obey, without any pay, you get a
   Cook and a nurse, for better or worse,
   You don't need a purse when a lady is sold.

7a But now that times are harder and my Jimmy's got the sack,
   I went down to Vicker's, they were glad to have me back,
   I'm a third-class citizen, my wages tell me that
   But I'm a first-class engineer!

b The boss he says, "I pay you as a lady,
   You only got the job 'cause I can't afford a man,
   With you I keep the profits high as may be,
   You're just a cheaper pair of hands!

c You got one fault: you're a woman,
   You're not worth the equal pay,
   A bitch or a tart, you're nothing but heart,
   Shallow and vain, you got no brain
   You even go down the drain like a lady today!"

8a I listened to my mother and I joined a typing pool,
   I listened to my lover and I put him through his school,
   If I listen to the boss I'm just a bloody fool
   And an underpaid engineer.

b I been a sucker ever since I was a baby,
   As a daughter, as a wife, as a mother, and a dear,
   But I'll fight them as a woman, not a lady,
   I'll fight them as an engineer!

Photograph by Jane Melnick

Emily

Words and Music by Julie Snow

We found Julie's songs in a fairly typical way--a friend said, "Oh, I have a friend who writes songs, and some good women's songs, you ought to ask her to sing them for you." We weren't prepared for the incredible music and words which were sung for us--a challenge to any of the pop-folk songwriters from Livingston Taylor to Joni Mitchell. Julie is another woman who has started playing and singing recently and has performed at Bread and Roses (a Boston women's restaurant and sometime cultural center) and other places, including the 1975 local Boston Women's Music Weekend.

Oh E- mi- ly——————— sits by her mo-ther's side, she looks in- to the clou- dy eyes that stare but do not see——— Sweet E- mi- ly, she said——— I hope that you won't mind if I sit here a- while in the dark to pass a lit- tle time——— it seems that I let go a long time a- go——— of all that bright and fir- ey spi- rit my own mo- ther swore she saw in me——— E- mi- ly——— E- mi- ly——— how the fire died is still a mys-ter-y— to me——— did I burn up all my dreams to sail an e- ven sea———

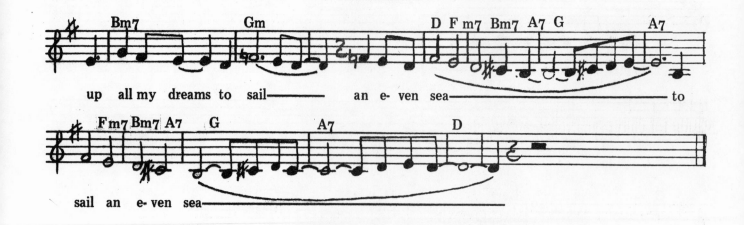

up all my dreams to sail———— an e- ven sea———————————— to

sail an e- ven sea——————————————————————

Julie Snow

Source: Heard in concert, Boston, 1975.

Women With Women

Centering our energies on other women has been the logical path for many of us who no longer have the energy to pretend or explain to men. Lavender Jane songs such as "A Woman's Love" express the joy in discovering love between women. Meg Christian's songs and many songs which were unveiled at the National Women's Music Conference in Illinois, ignore the world of men and celebrate the gay woman's experiences. "Invocation" is a mystical-matriarchal poem set to music--a reminder that women can again be as strong as they might have been in ancient societies where "they did not apologize." "The Armpit Song" is an affirmation for culture-controlled middle class women of what lots of other cultures and classes have known all along: "If pits were meant to be bare, then we would shed."

Photograph Courtesy Vermont Historical Society

A Woman's Love

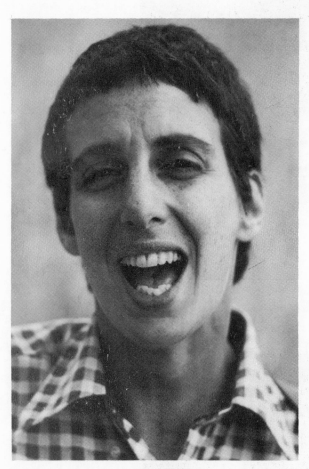

Alix Dobkin

It is hard for a heterosexual feminist to find traditional songs she can feel comfortable singing. It is hard for a lesbian to find traditional songs *or* contemporary feminsit songs that she can relate to. Lesbians share many battlefronts with all women, but there are some very real personal and political struggles that only lesbians must deal with. This song tells of the joyful resolution of one of those struggles.

Alix Dobkin has written many other songs in her own unique style; they can be found on the *Lavender Jane* album, and on her new album, *Living With Lesbians*.

Kay Gardner, who plays a sensuous flute on the album has produced a record on the Urana label (distributed by Olivia Records) called *Mooncircles*. It contains her own compositions of music for "circle dancing, meditation, and womanlove making."

A Woman's Love

Words and Music by Alix Dobkin

Be- cause she's a wo-man I did-n't think I loved her, so un- ex- pect- ed we just

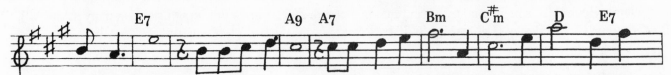

stood and smiled. and I felt so fine, and it was so right in- side, but how could I

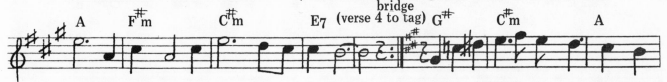

know I loved her be- cause she's a wo- man. I re- al- ize a wo- man's place is

my home ————. We've al- ways been in love and so it will be for Li— za

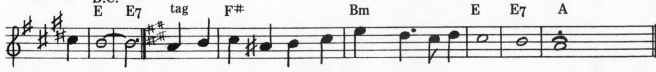

and me. and she feels so much the sweet touch of a wo- man's love.

2. Because she's a woman, confusion in my feelings,
I tried to name it everything but love,
But like a magic dream, it would not be turned aside,
But softly and warmly it held me,
Because she's a woman.

3. Because she's a woman, she doesn't try to change me,
She knows and understands a woman's ways,
And I feel so free to be what she sees in me,
It's so easy to be her lover,
Because she's a woman.

BRIDGE

4. Because I'm a woman, a way was laid out for me,
I always thought I'd need a man to love,
And while the men I've known were as loving as they could be,
There's no one can match her beauty, it's
Because she's a woman.

tag

And she feels so much the sweet touch of a woman's love.

We Don't Need the Men

Words and Music by Malvina Reynolds

Malvina has been active in singing for various struggles for many of her seventy years. Her "Little Boxes" song is perhaps her best-known song, and her most recent campaign has been to expose the brutality of the present Chilean government which killed Victor Jara, author of a Chilean version of that song. She lives on the west coast, but still tours and delights her audiences with her songs.

After you read through this song, take a look at the copyright date--1959! Some of us were escaping the Feminine Mystique after all!

Malvina Reynolds' songbooks and records can be ordered from Schroder Music Company (ASCAP), 2027 Parker St., Berkeley, California 94704.

It says in Cor- o- net Mag- a- zine, June nine- teen fif- ty six, page ten, that mar-ried wo- men are not as hap- py as wo-men who have no men. Mar- ried wo- men are crank-y frus- tra- ted and dis- gust- ed, while sin- gle wo- men are bright and gay, cre- a-tive and well ad- just- ed. We don't need the men. We don't need the men. We don't need to have them 'round, ex- cept for now and then. They can come to see us when we need to move the pi- an- o.
(v. 2) when they have tick- ets for the sym-pho-ny

Source: *Virgo Rising* LP, Thunderbird Records 7037 (97) (61).

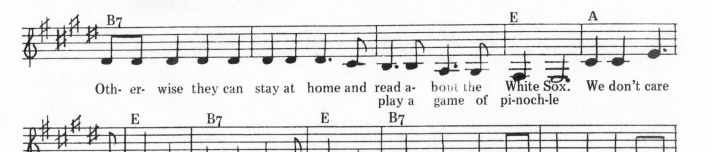

Oth- er- wise they can stay at home and read a- bout the White Sox. We don't care
play a game of pi-noch-le

a- bout them. We can do with-out them. They'll look cute in a bath- ing suit on a

bill- board in Man- hat- tan.

3. . . . when they're feeling pleasant and agreeable . . .
. . . holler at the T.V. programs . . .
. . . billboard in Madagascar . . .

4. . . . when they're all dressed up with a suit on . . .
. . . (spoken) drop towels in their own bathroom . . .
. . . billboard in Tierra del Fuego . . .

Photograph by Ethan Hubbard

71

Ode To A Gym Teacher

Words and Music by Meg Christian

Meg is one of the first feminist singers to record on the new feminist record label Olivia Records. She has recently been on a tour and sings everything from country-western to nostalgic pop tunes from the 1960's ("Sherry. . .won't you come out tonight")--some with a change of inflection, some totally tongue-in-cheek and other deadly serious.

Recently, she has started writing her own songs. Her background as a singer in clubs and bars gave her a lot of her easy way with an audience, but she has no show-offy "star" qualities which usually create distance between performer and audience. She now concentrates on exclusively women's audiences, and this song is a great example of a gay song which is first and foremost a gay song, not an old love song which underwent a gender-change.

As a member of the Olivia Records collective, Meg is involved totally in women's music and in continuing to analyze the liberating potentials of woman-controlled culture.

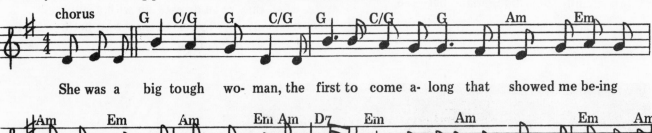

She was a big tough wo- man, the first to come a- long that showed me be-ing

fe- male meant you still could be strong. And tho' grad-u- a- tion meant that we had to

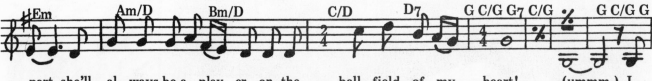

part, she'll al- ways be a play- er on the ball- field of my heart! (ummm-) I

wrote her name on my note pad and inked it on my dress. And I etched it on my

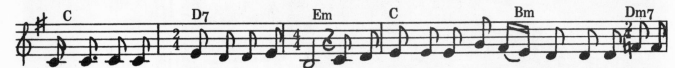

lock-er and I carved it on my desk. And I paint-ed big red hearts with her i- ni -tials

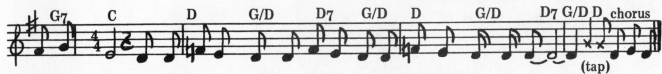

on my books. And I nev-er knew 'til lat-er why I got those fun- ny looks. She was a

2. Well, in gym class while the others talked of boys that they loved,
   I'd be thinking of new aches and pains the teacher had to rub.
   And when other girls went to the prom I languished by the phone
   Callin' up, and hangin' up if I found out she was home.

CHORUS

3. I sang her songs by Johnny Mathis, I gave her everything--
   A new chain for her whistle and some daisies in the spring,
   Some suggestive poems for Christmas by Miss Edna Millay,
   And a lacey, lacey, lacey card for Valentine's Day (unsigned,
      of course!)

CHORUS

4. So you just go to any gym class, and you'll be sure to see
   One girl who sticks to teacher like a leaf sticks to a tree,
   One girl who runs the errands and who chases all the balls--
   One girl who may grow up to be the gayest of all!!!

CHORUS

Photograph by Nancy Weschler

Source: *I Know You Know* LP, Olivia Records LF902 (52).

Talking Out of the Closet Blues

Words by Joyce Cheney
Music--Traditional

"This is a song about my experience of coming out. For anyone who's going through the process now, or thinks they may, there *are* hard parts to change; also lots of funny, up parts, and things folks never think of until it happens to them. Coming out certainly gets you to a nice place. Everything in the song is true-- including the part about the fortune teller."

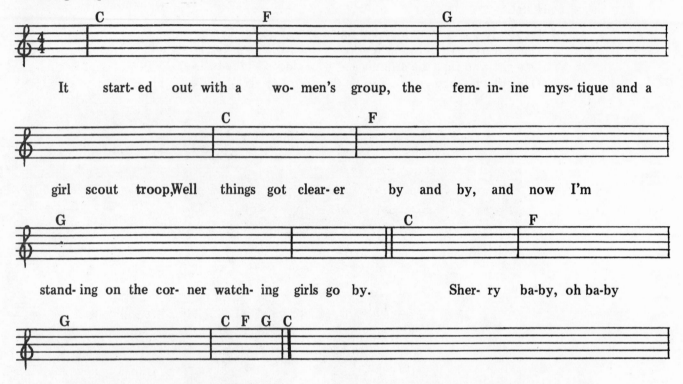

won't you come out to- night?

2. First I cut off both my braids,
   and my hair only hung to my shoulder blades.
   One more cut to my neck was fine,
   but the crew cut meant I'd crossed the line.
   (Out of the closet, Lavendar Menace, and
     into the streets.)

3. Well, it sheds new light on the institution
   of slumber parties; they're a contribution
   to future dykedom--so beware,
   tho' it's not co-ed--what's going on down there?
   (Kinda makes me wonder--about the nuns--locked up
     in convents.)

4. Well you can say you're roomates if you're keeping form,
   but you're getting kinda old for living in a dorm.
   Boogieing with women at a dance is o.k.
   It's the slow clingy ones that give us away.
   (They say gay liberation is one thing, but
     nobody likes a dyke.)

5. It amuses me the way things are fixed
   with public toilets where the sexes aren't mixed
   to guard against sexual vibes when you pee.
   But in a room full of women, between you and me,
   (Sometimes the ladies' room is where it's all at.)

Source: Heard in concert, Boston, 1974.

6. Well a girl on a building crew is o.k. now.
   So's Ms. Magazine and paying dues to N.O.W.
   You can hug your friend when you meet on the street,
   'cuz ladies' affection is safe and sweet.
   (But what if you want to kiss her on the lips--
       for ten minutes?)

7. Some straight folks panic and tear their hair.
   Some say it's o.k. for you, but I'm not there.
   But look in the closet and it'll be a surprise,
   A lot of friendly faces that you'll recognize.
   (You'll say, 'Whatcha doing here?" and they'll say--
       the same to you.)

8. When I was coming out I took a trip last year
   to a fortune teller my fortune to hear.
   I said, "Tell me, does my future look gay?"
   She said, "Nip it in the bud and hope it goes away."
   (Have you tried prayer, or therapy, or
       electrical shock?)

9. Well I don't get loose when I wear a dress.
   In a pair of pants I feel the best.
   It's kinda fun to have my preferences known
   when I wear my three-piece herringbone.
   (And nod at the woman in the subway car--who's
       wearing one too.)

10. So from humble beginnings in girls' P.E.
    to being a queer--it's happened to me.
    If it hasn't hit yet, just let the good vibes through.
    Loving women will make a dyke out of you.
    (Some of my best friends are, you know--
        what about you?)

Photograph by Jane Melnick

Invocation

Words and Music by Lanayre Liggera

The brutal torch-killing of a local Boston-area woman inspired this song. Its positive image of "moon-stains" captured the attention of Emily Culpepper, who used it on the soundtrack to her film on menstruation, "Period Piece."

For a biography of the composer, see "Sojourner Truth."

We— pu- ri- fy our-selves we wo- men. Rit- uals to a- tone for our as-

ser- tions. Hous- es al- ways clean-ly. Bod- ies al- ways pure. Souls dressed in new

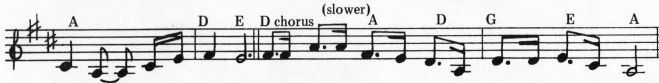

(slower)

bon- nets ev-ery East- er. I am old-er than this age. The moon calls forth my blood,

e- ven as it rules the o- cean tides. I dream of an- cient wo- men who did not

a- pol- o- gize for their moon-stains or their way of liv- ing. We pray their like

will come on earth a- gain. We

2. —purify ourselves, we women
Vessels for the guilts of all around us,
Faces averted, thoughts veiled in black,
Mourning for our goodness lost in Eden.

CHORUS

3. We purify ourselves, we women,
We are victims of the madman's crimes,
Hacked into pieces, thrown in unmarked graves,
Paying the full price for tributes rendered.

CHORUS

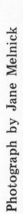

Photograph by Jane Melnick

Source: Heard in concert, Boston, 1974.

The Armpit Song

Words and Music by Ca Berman

Ca has performed her songs on Boston-area radio and at women's culture concerts. She has her own style of dazzling blue-jazz guitar picking which she incorporates into her original songs such as the one below and "Send Me Somebody to Squeeze Please."

Well I wear hair un-der my arms, 'cause it's real-ly soft and it keeps me warm, and I don't care what peo-ple say, for me arm-pit hair is the on-ly way. So I chucked all my ra-zor blades——. Arm-pit hair is hair to stay.

2. And I like the feel when it gets wet
   'Cause that's a part of me, my sweat,
   I let it grow and I don't regret
   So don't threaten me with your Gilette.

CHORUS

3. Without it I would feel so bare
   'Cause I really like havin' hair,
   And in the wintertime I would freeze, you know
   Armpit hair is no disease.

CHORUS

4. And most folks don't shave the hair from their heads
   If pits were meant to be bare then we would shed,
   And it's a lovely thing to have it there, for
   What's an armpit without the hair?

CHORUS

Photograph by Anne Pepper

Ca Berman

Source: Heard in concert, Emerson College, 1974.

Unfinished Business

This song pretty much speaks for itself. Unfortunately, the author can't. We feel it's important to acknowledge that, while this song voices a determined outcry against the repression of gay relationships in our society, that repression is a real and potent weapon. At times, anonymity is our only protection from traumatized family relationships, job discrimination and all of the other aspects of our daily lives that are jeopardized by the flow of our emotions.

Photograph by Bettye Lane

Source: Heard in concert, Boston, 1974.

Unfinished Business

Words and Music by I. M. Reluctant

I've got some un-fin- ished busi-ness. Well I just want to say- I've got

some un-fin- ished busi-ness to take care of to-day. Well I know what's on my

mind, and I think that it's time to tend the un- fin- ished busi-ness that

we left be- hind. Well they say that it's not nat- u- ral. They try to make you

scared to be a ho-mo-sex-u- al with feel-ings to share with a good friend

who it's plain to see is of the same sex that you just hap- pen to be.

2. Oh, it's so easy to run, it's so easy to hide,
It's so easy to find the ways to
Not find the time,
To dig my head out of the sand and
Look for the words
To answer the ones who say
We're out of our minds.

CHORUS

3. There's a feeling in my fingers like the
One in my heart, I want to
Reach out and hold you but I
Can't seem to start, 'cause my
Fear of sexuality just
Gets in the way, I'm
Paying for my fears and the
Price I got to pay is some

CHORUS

The Bloods

Words and Music by Deborah Lempke

The Berkeley Women's Music Collective performed "The Bloods" at the Women's Building in May of 1974 and stopped the show. It was also performed by the Clinch Mountain Backsteppers, a string band from the Northwest Coast, at the First National Women's Music Festival in Champaign-Urbana, Ill. in June, 1974.

Why, if kids grew up listening to songs like this about girls' periods, we bet all the little boys would wish they had one too! What with poems and movies about our periods, glorifying what was once whispered about and greeted with choruses or "ugh", this song may give a new definition to *rag*time music!

Source: *Berkeley Women's Music Collective Songbook* (18).

Well you might think this is lu- di- crous but when the moon is full I feel my
u- ter- us, and I know that the time's a- com- in', a-com- in' soon————. Some
sis- ters get down for men- stru- a- tion. Ain't no time for sad des- per- a- tion.
There's a new day com-in' when you got the bloods a- gain. Be-cause you
know your bod- y is a- work-ing al- right. If you had self- help you could watch
all night, get your spec- u- lum at the neigh-bor- hood clin- ic. Learn a-bout your
cer-vix and what's in it. There's a new day com-in' when you got the bloods a- gain.

2. If you're feelin' bad and you start to moan
Well, don't you hide, you're not alone
Cuz I know a time a-comin', a-comin' soon
When you're living together this I've found
That when the bloods come they come all way 'round,
There's a new day comin'
When you got the bloods again.

3. Men keep sayin' that the bloods are bad
Because it means you ain't fertile,
  that you ain't been had
But I know a time a-comin', a-comin' soon,
Men stop sayin' got to sleep with 'em
Cuz lesbians got natural rhythm,
There's a new day comin'
When you got the bloods again.

CHORUS

Ballad

Words and Music by Deborah Silverstein

Most of us probably grew up feeling like we could share our thoughts and feelings better with our best friend than with anyone else in the world--bemoaning the fact that our best friends were women instead of men, who we could have simply married and continued sharing thoughts and feelings with forever. And if that wasn't frustrating enough already, our best friend eventually *did* go off and get married. And who paid attention to the sorrow a friend feels when her closest companion slipped out of her life and into the expected security of a relationship with a man. It takes a long time to understand what was going on.

What's go-ing on, it lasts so long. Year af-ter year and the feel-ing's still strong. We be-came friends when we were so young. Seems we'll be friends our whole lives long.

2. I was so shy, you seemed so brave,
   Free to explore life, you showed me the way.
   I counted on you and you seldom betrayed,
   We grew in our friendship, our sorrows and play.

3. Boys were mysterious creatures to please,
   Mostly wrapped in fears and confusion for me--
   The romance and myth and fantasy--
   But I did not fear friendship and ours grew with ease.

4. Then you met a man, our world shifted around,
   History bound our priorities now.
   My loss and my sorrow I could not define,
   Seemed it was time to leave childhood behind.

5. The anger and pain, it drove me away,
   I could not comprehend what I could not name,
   You followed your man, how could I complain,
   What right did I have to demand the same?

6. Slowly we've come to realize
   The love that's threaded between our lives,
   That loving's as real with women as men,
   Soothed by time and changes our friendship will
                                              mend.

7. What's going on, it lasts so long,
   Year after year and the feeling's still strong.
   We became friends when we were so young,
   Seems we'll be friends our whole lives long.

Source: Heard in concert, Boston, 1974.

Garden Boogie

Words and Music by Joyce Cheney

"Here's a song for kids (young kids and grown-up kids). It's about two feminist musician-friends, who happen also to be green and leafy. The song came as a reaction to sexism and lack of positive female role models in kids' literature. It also came because I have a longstanding affection for good stories and for friendly vegetables (Vegetables will stand by you; we made some solid friends in the garden this year. Of course we ate them. . .)."

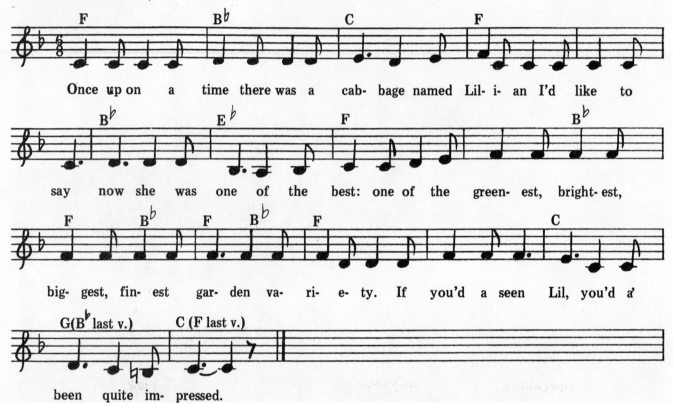

Once up on a time there was a cab- bage named Lil- i- an I'd like to
say now she was one of the best: one of the green- est, bright- est,
big- gest, fin- est gar- den va- ri- e- ty. If you'd a seen Lil, you'd a'
been quite im- pressed.

2. The next row down grew a grand cauliflower.
   She had firm green leaves and a big creamy head.
   She had a long, long name like "Cauliflower firmeous,"
   But all of the plants called her Hetty instead.

3. Now you may think that vegetables vegetate,
   Sit in the dirt and pine and sigh,
   But Hetty and Lillian had quite an active life,
   Plenty to do as the season went by.

4. They had tea with the worms and conversed with the snakes,
   They would chat with the bugs and the snails that came in,
   They'd sing with the birds and the sun would sing too,
   But when the moon came out, then the boogie'd begin.

Source: Heard in concert, Boston, 1974.

5. Then the squash would come jumping right off of the vine,
   Each punkin was wearing a wink and a grin,
   The broccoli was dancing right there in the row,
   And the onion was laughing and shedding its skin.

6. The peas were all popping right out of the pod,
   The beet stamped its feet, the tomatoes turned red,
   The carrots had care and the peppers had pep,
   And the lettuce was laughing and tossing its head.

7. The beans would all jump and the spinach would spin,
   All the potatoes were blinking their eyes,
   The corn came dressed in silk and perked up its ears,
   And out in that boogie--it was no surprise . . .

8. Was Lillian Cabbage singing rhythm and blues,
   Shaking her head to the beat of the song,
   And right beside her, they were closest of friends,
   Was Hetty M. Cauliflower, singing along.

9. You could hear the party from as far as the woods,
   Hetty and Lillian singing till dawn.
   But just about the time the stars were closing their eyes,
   The vegetables, one by one, started to yawn.

10. So with sleepy farewells and loving goodbyes,
    The party broke up, it was just getting light.
    Hetty and Lillian and all of their friends
    By the light of the moon had had a pretty good night.

11. So the next time you walk by the garden gate,
    Stop and see what you can see going on.
    If it looks like the plants are all resting and still,
    It's 'cause they just finished boogieing all night till the
       dawn.

12. Lillian Cabbage and Hetty M. Cauliflower,
    Side by side, growing best of friends.
    And all around are rows and rows and rows of friendly
       vegetables,
    And that's a good way for this tale to end.

Long Time Friends

Words and Music by Cathy Winter

"Singing 'Long Time Friends' has helped me realize that my hopes and needs are other people's as well, that a lot of people are looking for ways to open their hearts to an easier, better way of sharing and giving than their upbringing taught them to look for.

There's no song that is as much a pleasure for me to sing--because audiences don't just listen, they sing it, and everyone takes home a little bit of sharing."

Kathy is a singer, songwriter from Boston. She plays a great blues and bottleneck guitar and has recently begun to make her living from her music.

Well I'm look-ing for some long time friends I'm look-ing for some long-time friends

Life's a long and twist-ing road ma-ny curves and un-seen bends so I'm look- ing

for some long- time friends,
                1 Good friends tend to slip our of your reach,
2. There are wo- men that I hold close to my heart,

if you walk too tall and keep too straight a path   With your
and men I hope will al- ways be part of my life you've got to

eyes so far a- head that you can't see by your side you'll nev- er see your
know each heart is real and each life can touch your own and this world will be your

Long Time Friends
Long Time home.

Source: Heard in concert, Boston, 1975.

It's a wide world with many ways to live,
Many ways to love and ways to give.
I'm not so sure I want to find
Just one soul to blend with mine
So I'm looking for some long time friends.

Photograph by Martha Sempliner

Amelia Earhart

Historical Role Models

We often remain unaware of the accomplishments of women in the past--women in history are presented as a few axe-brandishing temperance fanatics or crazy suffragettes. "Elizabeth Gurley Flynn" and "Sojourner Truth" are about women who were political activists.

E.G. Flynn addressing a workers rally at Paterson, N.J. textile strike of 1913.

Elizabeth Gurley Flynn

Elizabeth Gurley Flynn is one of the outstanding figures from early 20th Century U.S. labor history. She was born in New England in 1890. Her ancestors were Irish "immigrants and revolutionists."

Elizabeth's parents were active socialists who included their children in their political life from the time they were babies. Elizabeth became an active participant in the socialist movement at the age of sixteen when she gave her first public address in front of the Harlem Socialist Club on the topic of "What socialism will do for women." Elizabeth spent the rest of her life fighting for the rights of all working people, later joining the Communist party. You can read the story of her life, and her first hand account of the labor movement in her autobiography, *Rebel Girl.*

Marge Cooper has been active in radical politics and the Women's Movement, working and living in Detroit, Michigan.

Elizabeth Gurley Flynn

Words and Music by Marge Cooper

E- liz- a- beth was a wo- man who could- n't be kept down. She was an or- gan- iz- er

who roamed from town to town, fight- ing with her sis- ters out on the pick- et lines,

build- ing us a fu- ture, E- liz- a- beth seized the time. Like E- liz- a- beth Gur- ley

Flynn, who nev-er did give in, gon-na build the rev- o- lu- tion and you know we're

gon- na win. Like E- liz- a- beth Gur- ley Flynn, who nev-er did give in, gon- na

build the rev- o- lu- tion and you know we're gon-na win!

2. Elizabeth was a woman, the bravest in her day.
   She fought for socialism, and she would always say,
   "We've got to get together, so we can all be free,
   We'll change the lives of women, and win our liberty."
   CHORUS

3. We've got to heed her message, for what she says is true,
   We'll join hands with our sisters in what we have to do,
   With working folk and young folk, red, white, black, yellow, brown,
   We'll build a people's movement, and tear the system down!
   CHORUS

Source: Redbasement Singers

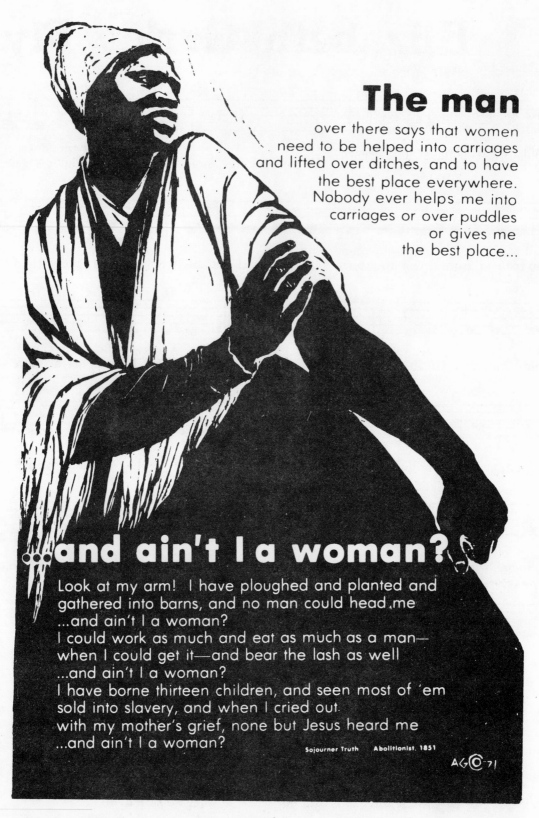

The man

over there says that women need to be helped into carriages and lifted over ditches, and to have the best place everywhere. Nobody ever helps me into carriages or over puddles or gives me the best place...

...and ain't I a woman?

Look at my arm! I have ploughed and planted and gathered into barns, and no man could head me ...and ain't I a woman?
I could work as much and eat as much as a man— when I could get it—and bear the lash as well ...and ain't I a woman?
I have borne thirteen children, and seen most of 'em sold into slavery, and when I cried out with my mother's grief, none but Jesus heard me ...and ain't I a woman?

Sojourner Truth   Abolitionist, 1851

AG©71

Poster by Ann Grifalconi

94

Sojourner Truth

Words Adapted from Sojourner Truth
Music by Lanayre Liggera

Sojourner Truth was a U.S. evangelist and civil rights pioneer. Born in Ulster County, N.Y. at the end of the 18th century, she was a slave until freed by her second owner. She then went on to win a court case to recover her son who was sold into slavery in the South, file the first slander bill brought by a Black against a white, and traveled around the country in support of abolitionists and later, women's rights. Her famous "Ain't I a Woman" speech occurred at a suffrage convention in Akron, Ohio in 1851. The words tell the story--she won over the convention.

Lanayre Liggera is 33, married for 11 years and has one child. She has been writing since she was a teenager, and has recently taken up the banjo, which she plays with the New Harmony Sisterhood Band. She has written a collection of feminist songs (see "Invocation" in this book) and taught a course in the Feminist Studies department at Cambridge Goddard Graduate School for Social Change in Women and Music during 1973-74. She is one of the main instigators and spiritual guides for this book.

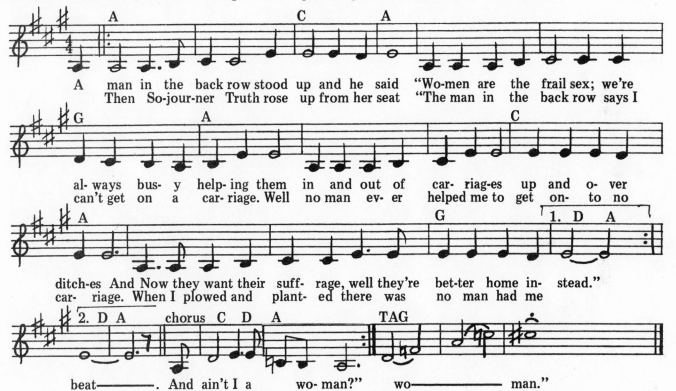

A man in the back row stood up and he said "Wo-men are the frail sex; we're
Then So-jour-ner Truth rose up from her seat "The man in the back row says I

al- ways bus- y help- ing them in and out of car- riag-es up and o- ver
can't get on a car- riage. Well no man ev- er helped me to get on- to no

ditch-es And Now they want their suff- rage, well they're bet-ter home in- stead."
car- riage. When I plowed and plant-ed there was no man had me

beat———. And ain't I a wo- man?" wo——— man."

3. "Look at my arm, I can work as much as you,
   And eat as much if I had food and bear the lash as well,
   No man did better, I have born thirteen children,
   I saw them sold to slavery and cried as mothers do,
   And ain't I a woman?"

4. "No man came to help me, only Jesus heard me,
   As I gathered into barns, no man eased my burden.
   When I cried in grief no man brought me back my children,
   Stand up again, mister, and take a look at me!
   And ain't I a woman,
   Ain't I a woman, woman." (CHORUS twice and tag)

Songs For Today's Activists

As we can learn from our sisters who struggled in the past to achieve the liberation of women at work and in politics, organized groups of women can make changes which will affect all women. The cultural activities of self-defining women accompany a changing status that women are creating in the economic and political arena. To argue which comes first, cultural or economic change, will have us balancing chickens and eggs on the head of a pin.

We can "name" our experience through our cultural expressions and give validity to our lives as *we* define them, and as we gain strength from this process of describing our own reality (and not accepting the spoon-fed media images), we can fight for changes. Women are not the only groups in this country who are left out of history and T.V. situation comedies. We owe it to other outcast groups in this country to be supportive. We know what it is to be written into history only as a stereotype. All of the songs in this section show women getting together in a politically active way in order to push for the world we envision--non-sexist, non-racist and non-classist.

Photograph by Jane Melnick

Nine to Five Song

Words by Jan Levine
Music--Traditional

Just like another song about Boston's M.T.A.'s which used this tune, this song pleads the case of Boston's white collar workers who must brave the public transit while "the boss drives a Mercedes." Nine to Five is an organization concerned with organizing clerical and secretarial workers in the Boston area--usually women who are underpaid and underpromoted. These jobs which once had more prestige than blue-collar jobs, are now being seen for what they are: jobs with a bit more status but less pay than unionized ones.

The Boston area organization for which this song was written, 9 to 5, has grown from a small group of women putting out a newsletter in 1972 to a veritable stone in the forehead of Boston's Goliath white collar employers. It has facilitated unions and published many studies which continue to fan flames in offices everywhere.

Let me tell you the sto-ry of a wo-man named Su- sie who ap- plied for a job

one day. They test-ed her for typ- ing, for short- hand and speed-writ-ing. Then

they gave her the low-est pay. We type and file from nine to five. Yet we bare- ly

stay a- live work-ing from day to day; Well we've done a day's work in the of- fi- ces

of Bos- ton and it's time we got a day's pay!

Source: *Nine to Five Newsletter*, Boston, (68).

2. Well then Susie did the filing
   And she kept the correspondence
   And she answered the telephone.
   Though the boss might be a doubter,
   Still he couldn't do without her,
   Wouldn't even call a taxi on his own.

   CHORUS

3. Susie asked for a promotion
   And she sure caused a commotion,
   He just looked at her in disbelief.
   But the raises they've been giving
   Sure don't match the cost of living
   Though the boss is still eating beef!

   CHORUS

4. Now the company makes millions
   And the boss drives a Mercedes,
   The oil crisis makes him frown.
   But he'll holler at a clerk
   If she is late to work
   'Cause the M.T.A. broke down!

   CHORUS

5. So Susie got together
   All the women in the office
   And they started to organize.
   If you thought women wouldn't fight
   For a basic worker's right
   Then you're in for a big surprise!

   CHORUS

6. Now you women of Boston
   Don't you think it's a crime
   That we suffer while employers thrive?
   Women's work is never done,
   Fighting back has just begun
   For a better life from nine to five!

Photograph by Helen McKenna

Ballad of Joan Little

Words by Kendall Hale
Music by David Green

Within the last year, nationwide attention has been focused on the trials of two women who did something unusual--protesting abuse by males who held sexual powers over them. Inez Garcia's case involved the killing of an accomplice in her own rape, and Joan Little, a black woman from North Carolina, was charged with murder in the slaying of her jailer. The chances for a young black woman to get a fair trial in the town where the jailer's family owned most of the property would have been pretty slim--had not women all over the country been outraged and prompted to organize and raise defense money.

Kendall writes, "I was inspired to write this song by Joan Little's struggle for freedom. A black woman, she refused to accept the fate racist, sexist America assigned her, by standing up and fighting back."

Although Karen Galloway's defense was brilliantly carried out, had it not been for the thousands of individual women who raised money for the defense, and who felt a sisterhood with Joan, this defense probably would not have been possible.

There are other songs about Joan Little. Bernice Reagon, who was one of the original Freedom Singers, who now sings with Sweet Honey in the Rock, and who will soon have an album out on Paredon Records, wrote a bluesy song about this same case. It appears in *Sing Out!* Vol. 24, No. 2 (May/June 1975). Alice Gerrard's song appears on Hazel and Alice's forthcoming new Rounder album, and "On the Line", a song about both Joan's and Inez Garcia's case, written by John D. Loudermilk and sung by Anne Romaine, appears on Anne's album, *Gettin' On Country*, Rounder 3009.

One night in a pris- on cell, a black wo-man used an ice pick to kill a jail- er who tried to rape her, tried to rape her. Jo- an Lit- tle met her fate. She was be- ing charged by the rac-ist state with mur-der, the first de- gree mur- der of Clar-ence Al-li- good. No one has the right to rape and ter- ror- ize black wo-men, an- y wo- man, black wo- men———. No one has the right to

rape and ter- ror- ize   black   wo- men,   an-y   wo- man,   black wo- men.

2. The prosecutor tried hard to put white male prison guards
Above the law, outside the law,
Above the law.
A former member of the Klan, he works with
Police and the businessman
Maintaining order, maintaining power,
The ruler's law.

CHORUS 2

Joan, by defending her dignity,
Helps us put an end to white and male supremacy.
Joan, by defending her dignity,
Helps us put an end to white and male supremacy.

3. They hid from the grand jury
That she fought violently before she
Struck him down, struck him down,
Struck him down.
Not just courtroom legality, it was the
Power of the people that freed
Joan Little, Joan Little,
Joan Little.

CHORUS 1

No one has the right to rape and terrorize
Black women, any woman,
Black women.
No one has the right to rape and terrorize
Black women, any woman,
Black women.

Photograph by Ellen Shub

Joan Little

Source: Heard in concert, Boston, 1975.

Still Ain't Satisfied

Words and Music by Bonnie Lockhart

"The Red Star Singers (Gary Lapow, Bonnie Lockhart, Ron Rosenbaum, and Mike Margulis) was formed (in 1971) out of the needs of four individuals to unify, share, and socialize our personal experiences as musicians and revolutionaries."

The Red Star Singers are no longer performing together, but you can still hear their music on *The Force Of Life*. Most of their performances took place in the San Francisco Bay area where they inspired their audiences with songs like "Belly of the Monster", "Pig Nixon", and others which you can learn from their album.

It's true--they got women doing most of the piggy things that only men used to do and we want something more--the total restructuring of the levels and hierarchies in present society, not just the top places in the ones we have now. But how wonderfully she puts it in this song!

Well they got wo-men on T.V. and I still ain't sat-is-fied, 'cause co-opt-a-tion's all I see,

and I still ain't sat-is-fied. They call me Ms.—. They sell me blue jeans, call it

"Wo-men's Lib." They make it sound ob-scene. And I still ain't—— woa, they lied—and I

still ain't—— woa, they lied, and I still ain't —— woa, they lied — and I still ain't sat-is-fied.

2. Well they got women prison guards,
But I still ain't satisfied
With so many still behind bars
I still ain't satisfied.
I don't plead guilt, I don't want no bum deal,
I ain't askin' for crumbs, I want the whole meal.

CHORUS

3. They liberalized abortion,
But I still ain't satisfied.
'Cause it still costs a fortune,
And I still ain't satisfied.
I'm singin' about control of my own womb,
And no reform is gonna change my tune.

CHORUS

Photograph by Jane Melnick

4. They give out pennies here and there,
   But I still ain't satisfied
   To set up centers for child care
   And I still ain't satisfied.
   And while we work at slave wages
   They brainwash our kids at tender ages.

CHORUS

I got some pride, and I won't be lied to.
I did decide that half way won't do.

103

Photograph by Jane Melnick

Self-Defense: Physical and Cultural

Men are also oppressed by the role models expected of them, but that does not counteract the ways in which women are oppressed physically and economically in ways that men are not. "I'm Tired of Fuckers Fucking Over Me" and "Woman in the City" paint the picture of a common experience to us all: walking down the street and being treated as entertainment (at best!) by male onlookers. "We Might Come In A-Fighting" expresses the important idea that we don't want to merely fit into the high slots that once were held by men, we want the entire structure of society to change: "When we enter in the game we're gonna change the goddamn rules." "All Our Lives" was written in response to a statement such as "You sing propaganda, and propaganda is not art! Why don't you have sympathy for the men who believe in Women's Lib?" As Deborah once said in a later introduction, "Let's hear it for propaganda!" There is enough noise made for the other side, but it is so prevalent that people don't consider *it* propaganda. If we don't look out for ourselves, we can hardly expect anyone else to.

I'm Tired of Fuckers Fucking Over Me

Words and Music by Bev Grant

Beverly Grant wrote this song in 1971. The women who put out the *Women's Songbook* changed the word "bastards" to "fuckers" because " 'bastards' means a woman must be legitimized only by a man, and a man is insulted by an insult to his mother."

Beverly had been through two marriages at the age of 24, went to work with Newsreel, a political film-making group, and took up the guitar. She has switched from writing exclusively feminist music, and concentrates on playing for and reaching the "non-organized" non-movement people who are being bombarded by a mass media which makes them feel inferior. Bev plays mainly around the New York City area.

When I'm walk-ing down the street, and ev-'ry man I meet says, "Ba- by,

ain't you sweet." I could scream——. But al- though those guys are sick and think

on- ly of their prick, it ain't sweet I feel; I just feel good and mean——. They whis-tle

for me like a dog and make nois- es like a hog. Heav- en knows they sure got

prob- lems I a- gree——. But their prob- lems I can't solve 'cause my san- i- ty's

in- volved, and I'm tired of fuck- ers fuck-in' o- ver me.

Bev Grant

2. When I'm tryin' to take a walk
   And some guy says he wants to talk
   And my way proceeds to block I get real sore.
   'Cause although I talk real fine
   That just ain't what's on his mind,
   I'm a pretty piece that he's just tryin' to score.

CHORUS

3. When I'm on my way to work
   And I'm confronted by some jerk
   Who's got some obscene quirk he must display,
   Though I know that guy is ill
   I can't help but want to kill
   Every other man who's standing in my way.

CHORUS

4. Now I know that life is rough,
   And to be a man is tough,
   But I have had enough and I can't ignore
   That their masculinity
   Just don't respect my right to be,
   And I solemnly do swear I'm goin' to war.

CHORUS

5. Well I sing this song in hope
   That you won't think that it's a joke,
   For it's time we all awoke to take a stand.
   We've been victims all our lives
   Now it's time to organize!
   To fight we're gonna need each others' hand.

CHORUS

Source: *Women's Songbook*, p. 26, (104).

Woman In The City

Words and Music by Julie Snow

For all of us who make our homes in the concrete jungle this song speaks to a frightening reality.
See "Emily" for a few words about Julie Snow.

I know —— you know —— what it's like —— to be a wo-man in the

ci- ty ——. Sounds like —— pigs and snakes fol-low right be- hind —— you

as you walk a- long the street ——. Should you stop to read a head-line——,or give

di- rec-tions to a stran- ger new in town; should you stop to watch a fire——

or pat a dog or pick a flow-er——, you may find you have a fol- low- er who feels

he has the charm or pow-er to win you or of-fend you with his words, to

breath in your face with his words——, to touch you if he wants to, to rub

up a-gainst you, and he'll tell you that it's your fault af- ter all he's just a man,

and men were made to get ex-ci-ted—— by a broad—— but it's that old

bi- o- lo—— gi- cal fraud—— fraud—— we just want to be left a- lone——

we just want to be left a- lone ——————

we just want to be left a- lone to walk or think or talk We just want to

be left a- lone—— I know—— you know—— what it's like——to be

a wo- man in the ci- ty——. I know—— you know too what it's

like—— to be a wo- man—— in the ci- ty——.

2. I know, you know, what it's like to be a
Woman in the city.
Locked in, locked out,
On guard from dusk until you turn the
Last light out.
Quite a rule book for behavior--
Your innocence depends on following the rules:
Always cover up your body,
Keep it stiff and well-supported,

Never walk down streets or hallways
That are empty or obscure.
Never speak to shady characters,
Never go thorugh the park at night,
Never look too free or happy,
Or they'll say that you asked for it,
You deserved just what you got.
After all is said and done, you're just a broad,
And you must buy the biological fraud.

Source: Heard in concert, Boston, 1975.

We Might Come In A-Fighting

Words and Music by Carolyn McDade

Carolyn McDade is a member and guiding spirit of the Arlington Street Women's Caucus, a group of about twenty women who came together through the Arlington Street Church in Boston. Their music is an affirmation of their belief that singing together is part of a "process which strengthens us, and which we know can strengthen others. This is the process of discovering, honoring, and rejoicing in our womanselves." Carolyn's music expresses an incredible mixture of strength and joy, determination and hope. Many of her songs have such a spiritual quality; it seems that perhaps Carolyn has celestial connections.

Recently the Caucus has produced a second album, *Leave the Breads A-Burning!* (the first was *Honor Thy Womanself*) and a songbook.

Well we might come in a fighting, 'cause there's lots that needs a-righting. We've learned a-lot from living never taught to us in schools. If they say come in like a man, well they must not understand. When we enter in the game we're gonna change the god-damned rules. Well they say if you enter in a man's world, there's got to be a boss, some-one a-giving orders, or it'll end in a total loss; But we know just from living that all folks got stuff for giving, and those hard lines of authority, we're bound to step across.

110

2. There somehow is this feeling we've got to work from nine to five--
   'Cause that's what makes a person worthy to be alive,
   Yet most of what they're doin' is bringing the world to ruin,
   We're gonna speed up with the living and slow down on the drive.

3. Well, I want it on the record that I think that something's wrong
   When some folks live in mansions, yet the poor work just as long.
   Well we're here a-realizing that there's lots of equalizing
   A-due in this world and we will help to move it on.

CHORUS

4. Well we say there's nothing more worthy than the caring for our young,
   Yet after we bear and raise them they will tell us one by one--
   Well, you can't come in expecting all the things a man is getting,
   'Cause looking at your record, there's nothing you have done.

Photography by Marilyn J. Boyer

Arlington St. Women's Caucus

5. Now what is more important in the life of anyone,
   A-talking with some friends or all the memos you have run
   That are knee-deep you know where the forest used to grow-
   Now the making of more garbage just ain't worth a-being done.

CHORUS

   Now we're here for to tell you--gonna say it out so strong--
   We want work worthy of doing and some time to call our own.
   They may think we'll sweetly smile and be glad to wait awhile--
   Won't be no feminine bargaining--that day has come and gone.

CHORUS

Source: *Honor Thy Womanself* LP, Rounder 4006 (48).

All Our Lives

Words and Music by Deborah Silverstein

I wrote this song in response to the following experience: There was a party one night after a concert where our band had played some feminist songs. A man came up to me at the party, a little drunk, and said that he really liked our music; and he really sympathized with the women's movement; BUT, he protested that our songs left him out. "Why didn't we do some love songs too?" After all, if you aren't expressing all aspects of human experience, then you're really doing propaganda, not art!

It was a very frustrating conversation. Unfortunately, one simple and basic point escaped me at the moment: much of what is presented to us under the label of "art" is propaganda from a sexist point of view.

The men lis-ten and then say, "I'm sym-pa-thet-ic babe. I know what you wo-men

have been through, all your lives. But I'm not the one to blame, I did-n't write the

rules to this lous-y game. But you've got no-thing for us men al-read-y on your

side." Well you want to see some sweet-ness, not just streams of an-gry words. You

real-ly dig the mus-ic but the mes-sage is too tough. It seems like we've for-got-ten a-

bout hap-pi-ness and love. You think we've said what we had to say but e-nough's e-nough.

Source: Heard in concert, Boston, 1974.

2. Well I understand their point, they don't think we should exploit
   The first chance we've ever had to fight back all our lives,
   We're told to soften our approach, let some tender feelings show,
   And give our sympathizers equal time.

   CHORUS

3. Well I've only this to say, I look forward to the day
   When women won't have to fight for an equal chance all their lives,
   And the purpose of our songs is to move this fight along
   Until there's room for more than just the struggle to survive.

   CHORUS LAST TIME:
   It's not that we've forgotten about happiness and love
   But until the times have changed it's not enough.

New Harmony Sisterhood Band

Papa

These feminist lyrics were set to the blues song "Keep On Truckin' Mama" and are the answer to the male music world's objectification of women--"Back Street Girl, Under My Thumb." The rest of the record contains more songs by the Chicago Women's Liberation Rock Band (now defunct due to problems of commitment, see Naomi Weisstein's article in *Paid My Dues*, Vol. I, No. 2) on one side and by the New Haven Women's Liberation Rock Band (changed but still with us) on the other.

This record was the first strong self-consciously feminist music. Most of it is hard to reproduce for singing in the folk idiom, but luckily this song calls for lots of singing and stomping and can be done without the need for rock equipment.

Source: *Mountain Moving Day* LP, Rounder 4001 (63).

Papa

Words by Naomi Weisstein and Virginia Blaisdell
Music--Traditional

Keep on truck-in', ma-ma, truck-in' all the live-long day. Keep on truck-in', ma-ma,

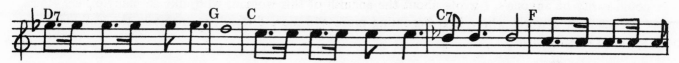

truck-in' all your cares a- way. Wake up in the morn-ing. Wake up late. Down to the cor-

ner to get your-self a date. (If ya) Can't stop do-ing what you do to me, you're

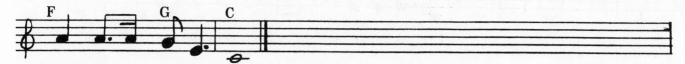

just gon-na drive me wild!

2. Papa don't lay that shit on me, it just don't compensate,
   Papa don't lay that shit on me, I can't accommodate.
   You bring me down, It makes you cool,
   You think I like it you're a goddamn fool,
   Papa don't lay that shit on me, It just don't compensate.

3. Papa don't lay those sounds on me, I ain't your groovy chick.
   Papa don't lay those sounds on me, don't you know they make me sick.
   Rolling Stones, Blood, Sweat and Tears,
   I've taken that shit for too many years,
   Papa don't lay those sounds on me, I ain't your groovy chick.

4. Papa I ain't your friend no more, ain't gonna make your bed.
   Papa I ain't your friend no more, better get a dog instead.
   Back Street Girl, Under My Thumb,
   Start looking out where you're coming from,
   Papa I ain't your friend no more and I ain't gonna make your bed.

5. Papa don't lay that shit on me, you just don't turn me on.
   Papa don't lay that shit on me, the fun and games are gone.
   It wasn't my fun,
   All that trashing is over and done,
   Papa don't lay that shit on me, you just don't turn me on.

6. (Repeat first verse)

Abortion

Words by Deborah Silverstein
Music--Traditional

It is difficult to choose a few words of introduction to a topic which is the basis of significant moral and philosophical debate. Few issues have the power to create such violent conflict among women as the right to abortion. I wanted to write a song that could reach beneath the superficial characterization, so widespread in the media, of pro-abortionists vs. right to lifers. So, I wrote about one woman's experience. Her story could easily be anyone's. I wrote about the anguish of this woman, who, like so many others, finds herself pregnant in a world where it is becoming more and more difficult to maintain the well-being of those who are already alive.

I al-ways done right by my friends and my fam-ily don't seem to mat-ter trou-ble knows where to find me I ain't ne- ver———— no ne- ver been sa- tis- fied. All the folks on the hill they're so self-right-eous they'll be scream-in shout-in that I'm sell- ing my soul Well all these folks they show so much con-cern be -fore the ba-by is born But once you're a- live they don't real- ly care if you live or die

116

live or die live or die I ain't nev- er no ne- ver

been sat- is- fied.

We spent ten years treadin just to keep above water,
Now my husband lost his job and we're goin under.
I ain't never, no never, been satisfied.

My heart's about to break, the kids are cryin from hunger
I already got five, now I'm carrying another.

That crying don't lie, it's drivin me wild
Lord what'll I do I can't feed another child?
I ain't never, no never, been satisfied.

I been tossin all night, light's breakin for morning,
But I settled my peace, I'm gonna get an abortion.

Source: Heard in concert, Boston, 1976.

Juanita

Words and Music by Marian McDonald

Marian is one of those singer-songwriters who wasted some of the best years of their lives believing what that fourth grade teacher said about "mouth the words--don't sing." She has written many fine songs such as this one, "Women Friends", "Song to My Mother", and "The Marriage Song." She has recently started performing in the Boston area.

She wrote this song after the experience of meeting Juanita at the Red Book, a leftist bookstore in Boston. She says, "I would like to dedicate this song to the Chilean people, especially to the Chilean cultural workers who continue to struggle bravely against repression and who provide great inspiration for cultural workers from all over the world."

Oh Juan-i-ta, you stepped down from the Grey-hound bus to be-gin all o-ver,

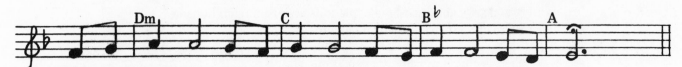

with your daugh-ter, young as free-dom, and your sor-row, dark as night.

Take my hand, sis-ter Juan-i-ta, and we will go to fight to-geth-er. The

way we're mov-ing is the same way. So-cial-ist Chi-le will rise a-gain.

2. Oh, Juanita, your friends are dying
   In prison cells and in city streets--
   You hear their rage and you hear their crying
   And how it echoes in your eyes.

CHORUS

3. Oh, Juanita, for nineteen years now
   This country's raped you with all its lies.
   But now you know that the only truth is
   In the deep clear sound of your battle cry.

CHORUS

4. Oh, Juanita, you now are homeless,
   Without a paycheck to erase your hunger,
   But you've a spirit stronger than all their killing,
   And it spreads like fire, and it shines like light.

   CHORUS (Repeat: Socialist Chile will rise again!)

Source: Heard in concert, Boston, 1976

Traditional Songs

A few of the songs in this section were written recently. We put them here because they were particularly appropriate to these categories.

Traditional Love Songs

These are *not* the type of songs we want to emphasize in this book. They are taken care of quite well in most other songbooks and in some women's workshops at well-meaning folk festivals, coffee houses and records. When "women's songs" are mentioned, the first thought to arise is usually that of a song like "John Riley"--exemplifying the waiting woman who lives for her long-lost lover. We can't wish away these stereotypes, nor can we deny that some women still fit them. But the need is to *expand* on this definition of womankind, and use these songs as teaching devices that show their limitations of roles for women.

John Riley

Collected, Adapted, and Arranged by John A. Lomax and Alan Lomax

"John (or George) Riley" is presumed to have derived from a broadside sheet, published in a Dublin songbook of 1791, entitled "The Constant Damsel." The song has travelled and changed, borrowing elements from and intertwining with "The Broken Token" and "Phoebe and Her Dark-Eyed Sailor."

The young woman passes the test of fidelity, but one can't help but wonder if she loved him so much, not to have recognized him after three years.

As I walked out one morn- ing ear- ly, to breathe the sweet and pleas- ant air, who

should I spy but a fair young maid- en, whose cheeks were like the li-ly fair?

2. I stepped up to her and kindly asked her
   If she would be a sailor's wife.
   "O, no, kind sir, I'd rather tarry
   And remain single for all my life."

3. "What makes you so far from all human nature?
   What makes you so far from all human kind?
   You are young, you are youthful, fair and handsome,
   You can marry me if you're so inclined."

4. "The truth, kind sir, I'll plainly tell you,
   I could have married three years ago
   To one John Riley who left this country
   Who has been the cause of my grief and woe."

5. "Come along with me, don't think of Riley
   Come go with me to a distant shore.
   We will set sail for Pennsylvany,
   Adieu to England for evermore."

6. "I'll not go with you to Pennsylvany,
   I'll not go with you to a distant shore;
   For my heart is with Riley and I can't forget him,
   Although I may never see him no more."

7. N'w when he saw that she loved him truly,
   He gave her kisses one, two, three,
   Saying, "I am Riley, your long-lost lover,
   Who has been the cause of your misery."

8. "If you be he and your name be Riley,
   I will go with you to that distant shore,
   We will set sail for Pennsylvany,
   Adieu to England for evermore."

9. They locked their hands and their hearts together,
   And to the church house they did go,
   And they got married to one another,
   They're living together, doing well.

Source: *Folksongs of Peggy Seeger*, p. 39, (37). Also: (36), (55), (80).

Motherhood

There are motherhood songs which imprison us on a pedestal; there are a few mother songs that tell us realistically what it is like. Many mother songs are literally Madonna songs--Christian songs that have a male savior and a Holy mother. Then there are the secular Madonna songs, which outline the standards mothers are supposed to live up to. Women were romantically idealized for good reason. In a time when the farm had to be run by a community of people, women's bodies produced a valuable commodity--more people. Woman's importance in a pioneer society is summed up by Erik Erikson:

The American woman in frontier communities was the object of intense rivalries on the part of tough and often desperate men. At the same time, she had to become the cultural censor, the religious conscience, the aesthetic arbiter, and the teacher. In the early rough economy hewn out of hard nature, it was she who contributed the finer graces of living, and that spirituality without which the community falls apart.[1]

Mother served as a conscience allayer for men. Mother became the super-ego, the conscience to whom devotion is offered up as a penitential ritual for male oppression. This conscience, however, usually forgives.

In bluegrass music, the ideal mother is a dead mother. Death obscures individual characteristics; the mother-figure can then project archetypal maternal sweetness and impart motherly admonitions that the singer either longs to hear or cannot escape. In "Mother, the Queen of My Heart" (see reference list 54) we see the idea of mother as super-ego brought to a chilling ending. In later mother songs, the moral arbiter role fades, as institutions take on more responsibility for socialization of children. She becomes the idealized mother--sweet, uncritical and completely accepting, more like the passive love-object. In "The Sweetest Gift A Mother's Smile" total forgiveness is exemplified.

The lullaby "What'll I Do With This Baby-O" is sung by the mother, and not about her, and is closer to some of the real feelings of all mothers at times. Most mother songs are set within the context of a proper nuclear family. There are also plenty of songs about women who find themselves becoming mothers without the support of the approved social structure. Many of the complaint songs under the "Beware Young Ladies" category touch on the disappointments of marriage and motherhood.

As more women work out ways of integrating the option of motherhood into contemporary feminist lifestyles, we'll begin to see music that reflects the breakdown of the "Supermom" myth. Alix and Kay of Lavender Jane have many strong and forceful songs and they integrate some involvement of their children into their music--a good sign!

[1]Erik Erikson, *Childhood and Society*, New York: Norton, 1950, pp. 291-292.

The Sweetest Gift A Mother's Smile

Words and Music by J.B. Coates

The total forgiveness of the mythical mother is manifested here--"It did not matter what he had done." This song was probably widely sung around the 1930's and '40's on early records and radio. This version, sung by Hazel and Alice, was inspired by the Blue Sky Boys on a Victor recording done in 1949.

2. Her boy had wandered far from the fireside,
   Though she had pleaded with him each night;
   Yet not a word did she ever utter,
   That told her heartaches, her smile was bright.

   CHORUS

3. She left a smile you can remember;
   She's gone to heaven from heartaches free;
   The bars around you will never change her,
   You were her baby and e'er will be.

   CHORUS

Source: *Hazel and Alice* LP, Rounder 0027 (45).

What'll I Do With This Baby-o?

As sung by Jean Ritchie

Jean Ritchie writes in *Singing Family of the Cumberlands* that often all the neighbors would get together for a quilting or a night of singing and playing games, and all the babies would be put away in one room. Someone often had the job of singing them to sleep, and this lullaby was a favorite.

Other versions have such verses as "Throw the baby against the wall" or "Wrap him up in a tablecloth, Throw him in the old hayloft." It certainly seems more true-to-life for a woman who is surrounded all day by babies to get a chuckle out of *these* words as she changes diapers--not some frothy pink-and-blue pap about angels from heaven!

What-'ll I do with this ba- by-o? What-'ll I do with this ba- by- o? What-'ll I

do with this ba- by- o, if he don't go to sleep- y- o? Wrap him up in cal- i- co.

Wrap him up in cal- i- co. Wrap him up in cal- i- co. Send him to his mam-my- o.

2. What'll I do with this baby-o,
   What'll I do with this baby-o,
   What'll I do with this baby-o,
   If he won't go to sleepy-o?
   Wrap him up in a tablecloth,
   Wrap him up in a tablecloth,
   Wrap him up in a tablecloth,
   Throw him up in the fodder-loft.

3. What'll I do, etc.
   Tell your daddy when he comes home,
   Tell your daddy when he comes home,
   Tell your daddy when he comes home,
   And I'll give Old Blue your chicken bone.

4. What'll I do, etc.
   Pull his toes, tickle his chin,
   Pull his toes, tickle his chin,
   Pull his toes, tickle his chin,
   Roll him up in the countypin.

5. What'll I do, etc.
   Dance him north, dance him south,
   Dance him north, dance him south,
   Dance him north, dance him south,
   Pour a little moonshine in his mouth.

6. What'll I do, etc.
   Everytime the baby cries
   Stick my finger in the baby's eye!
   That's what I'll do with the baby-o,
   That's what I'll do with the baby-o.

Source: *Celebration of Life*, p. 15, (23).

Jean **Ritchie**

The Beginning

Words and Music by Karen Burt

When labor begins, the uterus--a big muscular bag--begins to contract regularly--at first many minutes apart, then, gradually, more often. And the contractions themselves last longer. The purpose of the contractions is to slowly open, or "dilate" the entrance to the uterus (the cervix) so that the baby, head first usually, can slip through. An early sign of labor is when mucous that has plugged up the cervix during pregnancy, loosens and slips out (through the vagina). It is usually blood-tinged and therefore called the "bloody show". Another event in labor is the "water breaking"--when the thin fluid filled sac surrounding the baby inside the uterus, breaks from the action of the contractions--and the fluid leaks (or gushes) out. The hardest part of labor--when the contractions are most frequent and last longest--is when the cervix is dilating the last few centimeters (from about 8 to 10. 2½ cm. = 1 inch) stretching over the baby's head. During this time a woman may feel shakey, nauseous, hot, cold, emotional, or irritable. Fortunately, this period, called "transition" is usually short. It is followed by a spontaneous urge to push with each contraction to help get the baby through and out of the vagina. Sometimes the urge to push comes too early--when the cervix is almost but not quite over the head yet. Though it is very difficult--a woman must try not to push until she is fully dilated. When about a quarter's size amount of the baby's head can be seen at the vaginal opening, it is called "crowning", and it is usually at this time in a hospital that the laboring woman is transferred to the delivery room where the baby is soon born.

Prepared childbirth, or natural childbirth, includes ways of relaxing, concentrating, and breathing during the different stages of labor, usually breathing shallower and faster as the labor progresses. Perhaps most important is that a woman is not left alone, she has someone with her (often called the "coach") to help her with breathing and relaxing, to give her support and love. And thus a woman also has the opportunity to be sharing her experience of childbirth.

There is a growing movement in this country by women to take control of reproduction out of the hands of doctors alone. Abortion and contraception rights, and the challenging of sterilization abuse are parts of this movement. Prepared and natural childbirth are another. The resurgence of midwifery and homebirths another.

Women must have the right to control their own bodies.

Karen lives in Boston, is a medical student, and a member of the Red Basement Singers.

I was woke up last night by a pain in my belly, did- n't need no one to tell me that I ne- ver

felt the same. I got really ex- ci- ted cause I knew my time'd a- rrived sure e-nough now each ten

min-utes the same feel-ing'd by re-vived. O my wo-man's work is just be-gun, breathe nice and slow,

130

star-ing moon eyed at the wall un- till the tight-ness goes. Well I know I'll love that lit-tle babe no

mat-ter when she come, hope it's soon-er and not lat-er — O yea hur- ry lit- tle one.

2. Now the pains are coming stronger but we're riding nice and high.
   I'm just sucking on my ice chips and enjoying my massage.
   Hey this labor ain't so bad — the contractions in a row
   Every five minutes now and I just had a bloody show.

O my woman's work is in full swing
Breathing in and out
Staring moon eyed at the wall
To pass away the night.
Well I know I'll love that little babe no matter when he come
Hope it's sooner and not later — O yea hurry little one.

3. We got us to the hospital but the labor's getting worse
   Lord I thought this job was easy; O my God my water's burst!
   But my coach says, "You can do it — six centimeters now!"
   Then breathes me back in rhythm and mops my sweaty brow.

O my woman's work is long and sure
Breathe at a faster pace
Staring moon eyed at the wall
Or at my coach's face.
Well I know I'll love that little babe no matter when she come
Hope it's sooner and not later — O yea hurry little one.

4. Turn on this side then on that one — sit up and lay back down
   The pains are every minute and really gone to town.
   And I've got the wildest shaking and I'm just about to heave
   And I'm feeling kinda nasty cause I wish that I could leave!

O a woman's work is never done
Pant-blow for dear life
Staring mooneyed at the wall
If I'd known what this was like!
Well I know I'll love that little babe no matter when he come
Hope it's sooner and not later — this transition ain't no fun.

5. O my God I got this feeling from my head down to my toes
   Like an urgent need to bear right down until the feeling goes.
   Yes I gotta push this baby out and get this feeling gone
   But they tell me that I gotta wait — not far enough along.

O will a woman's work be ever done?
Blow, blow, blow, blow out
It's hell on earth not to push
Of that I have no doubt.
Well I know I'll love that little babe no matter when she come
Hope it's sooner and not later — O yea hurry little one.

6. Hallelujah Hallelujah now I'm fully dilated
   I can push to my heart's content to get my babe created.
   This may be the hardest work I ever did but sure feels great.
   I'm exhausted but provided now with four minute breaks.

O my woman's work is almost done
Pushing with all my might
Bearing down and turning red
The head is just in sight
Well I know I'll love that little babe no matter when he come
Hope it's sooner and not later — O yea hurry little one.

7. The baby's head is crowning; the delivery's coming soon
   Looking in the mirror at the wet and shiny dome
   Squeezing slowly out of me — My mind is in a whirl
   Now the head . . . now the shoulders . . . now the body . . . O my love — it's a girl

O a woman's work is ended
Or perhaps just begun
Staring moon eyed at my babe
In the morning sun.
Well I know we love this little babe: we're happy that she's come . . .
O yea Welcome little one.

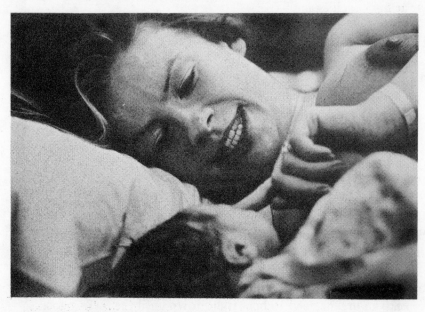

Photograph by Miriam Weinstein

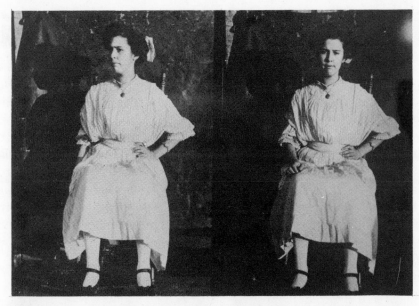

Shrewish Women

The tale goes that our sisters in the past all wanted to get married. Indeed, they did, for they saw no other feasible way to survive. And the songs have generally reinforced romantic notions of love and marriage, rather than exploding them. More and more married women today have the option of making a positive and independent change for themselves. But it has only been in the very recent past that women have had the option of getting out of a marriage at all respectably. Until recently, the choices have been all negative: make do, leave the family and be a social outcast, cease functioning as expected (through insanity or various illnesses) or turn into an unacceptable woman--a shrew.

There is a whole genre of song and folktale about these women, who didn't acquiesce to housewifedom so graciously. As a shrew, a woman certainly got to act out her frustrations, but it didn't change the fact that she was still a domestic slave. Her shrewishness compounded the problem by making her a clown--an object of social and familial ridicule. Her actions were not viewed as justified rebellion, but as personal foibles.

None of the shrew songs mention what demands were put on the wife--besides housework, sexual fidelity and domestic chores--nor do they mention what calmer ways she'd tried to affect changes before she "banged him with the coal shovel round the room at night." Shrewish women were sabateurs who hadn't found a collective solution. They were individuals working before the awakening of women's collective consciousness to sabatoge their oppressive situations.

Shrewish songs are all double-edged; they can be taken as positive songs about spunky women who fought back, or as tongue-in-cheek mockeries of women who were not socially correct. The farmer's wife in "The Farmer's Curst Wife" had a lot of strength and spunk--even the devil couldn't handle her-- but what sort of praise is it to be too outrageous for hell? Most of these songs probably came about as mockeries. This ridicule, stemming from hatred and fear of women with power (witness the mass execution of witches, who are now being hailed as the poor person's alternative to the beginnings of the medical-business establishment) kept many a socially aberrant female in her place.

It is not far in visual imagery from a housewife sweeping to a witch riding a broom. Perhaps witchdom is the open affirmation of the doubts and suspicions harbored against us as a group--that we are all possessed, uncontrollable and somehow tapping other forces.

We are accused of being humorless if we don't laugh too. We *can* laugh, but we can't *just* laugh at them and not think about them. They are a part of our self-concept and help mold us. We need to understand that these songs are not just healthy humor, that they have a political side which reinforces outmoded ideas about women.

The Farmer's Curst Wife

Traditional

This song, also called "The Devil and the Farmer's Wife" is a common theme in traditional lore. A woman on a farm was supposed to do the work uncomplainingly and unceasingly and if she didn't she was likely to inspire an attitude which produced a song such as this.

"In the original medieval story we find an impoverished farmer desperately trying to till his land with a swing hitched to a plow. He cannot spare his son's labor, but gladly gives up his shrewish wife to the Devil. She thereupon turns Hell upside down, and, in many American versions, returns to earth to paddle her old man's head with the butter-stick, to bully-rag him and, in some versions, to march away over the hills, cheerfully whistling her devil's ditty. American Calvinist men, whose feminine house-slaves had been robbed of their sensuality, unconsciously recognized the extent of their tyranny, and were afraid. In the Ozarks, if a man divorces his first wife and marries again unhappily, they say, "He's swapped a witch for the Devil."
--from *Folk Songs of North America*, p. 174.

Another version ends:

    This proves women are worse than men,
    They get sent down to hell and get throwed out again.

There was an old man who lived o- ver the hill, Oh, dad-dy, be gay, There was an old

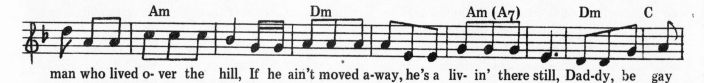

man who lived o- ver the hill, If he ain't moved a-way, he's a liv- in' there still, Dad-dy, be gay

and eat can- dy.

2. The Devil, he come to his field one day,
   Says, 'your old wife I'm gonna take away.'

3. 'O take, O take her with all of my heart,
   And I hope to my soul that you'll never part.'

4. So he took the old lady all up in a sack,
   And off to Hell he went clickety-clack.

5. When he got her down 'bout half of the road,
   He says, 'Old lady, you're a devil of a load.'

6. And when he got her to the gates of Hell,
   Says, 'Punch up the fire, I'm gonna scorch her well.'

7. Nine little devils come a-draggin' a chain,
   She took it away and she knocked out their brains.

8. Ten little devils went a-climbin' the wall,
   Says, 'Take her back, daddy, she's a-murdrin' us all.'

9. She found the old man lyin' late in his bed,
   She picked up the butter-stick and paddled his head.

10. Away she went whistelin' over the hill,
    'If the devil won't have me, I wonder who will?'

11. That goes to show what a woman can do,
    She's worse than the Devil and she's worse than you.

From *Folk Songs of North America*, Ed. by Alan Lomax   Collected by John Lomax; Recorded and Arranged by Alan Lomax   New York: Doubleday, 1960.   Used by Permission

Source: *Folk Songs of North America*, (36). Also: **(25)**, (11), (15), (5).   "The Devil and the Farmer's Wife" in (93).

Ballad of Susanna Martin

Words and Music by John Allison

The setting: 1692, in Salem, Massachusetts. Belief in witches is rampant. Belief that young women are hysterical, emotional and irrational is also rampant. A group of teenage girls become possessed by the Devil through the work of witches and point out the women in the town who are witches. These women are taken to trial, and most--20--are executed for their involvement with the Devil.

Susanna Martin was one of those executed. She was charged, among other things, with bewitching John Allen's oxen, and causing them to swim out to sea. Cotton Mather was a fire-and-brimstone theologian who came to Salem during the witch trials.

The words to this song were adapted from the Salem witch trial transcripts of May, 1692 and the tune is to be done in the manner of an ancient modal melody. John Allison, who wrote the tune and words, is among the pioneer researchers in the realm of musical Americana. He produced the *Witches and War Whoops* record from which we got this song.

2. A witch was she, tho' trig and neat with comely head held high,
   It did not seem that one as she with Satan so would vie.
   And when in court, the afflicted ones proclaimed her evil ways,
   She laughed aloud, and boldly then met Cotton Mather's gaze.

3. "Who hath bewitched these maids?" he asked, and strong was her reply,
   "If they be dealing in black arts, ye know as well as I!"
   And now the stricken ones made moan as she approached near,
   They saw her shape upon the beam, so none could doubt 'twas there.

136

4. The neighbors 'round swore to the truth of her Satanic powers,
   That she could fly o'er land and stream and come dry shod thro' showers.
   At night, 'twas said, she had appeared a cat of fearsome mien,
   "Avoid, She Devil!" they had cried to keep their spirits clean.

5. The spectral evidence was weighed, then stern the parson spoke,
   "Thou shalt not suffer a witch to live, 'tis written in the book!"
   Susanna Martin, so accused, spake with flaming eyes,
   "I scorn these things for they are naught but filthy gossip's lies!"

6. Now those bewitched, they cried her out, their voices loud did ring,
   They saw a bird above her head--an evil yellow thing;
   And so Susanna Martin died beneath a summer sky,
   And still in scorn she faced the rope--her comely head held high.

Source: *Witches and War Whoops* LP, Folkways 5211 (100).

In Praise of John Magee

Wife-selling was quite common in England between 1750 and 1860, and this Irish ballad documents that it occurred in Ireland as well. The wife auction seems to have been a highly ritualized affair and not just the drunken event described by Thomas Hardy in *Mayor of Casterbridge*. The selling was done in the market place, where the woman was led with a halter around her neck or waist. The deal was then concluded over a drink and included the signing of the papers. Ashten quotes from the Wales *Daily News* for May 2, 1882 that a man parted with a wife for a glass of ale.

Sometimes the wife was sold to her lover, in this case, she is bought by "a neighbor of her own" and in some cases, the wife even sold the husband. Divorce required an Act of Parliament, and cost lots of money, so wife-auctioning was a crude form of divorce, the only one available to the lower classes. Nevertheless, the parallels between slavery and marriage are not too far-fetched when we realize that the husband had such control over his property (wife) that he could sell her like a slave!

Courtesy Vermont Historical Society

138

For I'll sing in praise of John Ma- gee who was auc- tion- ing his wife. She was a hard

work- ing wo- man but the dev-il all her life. Nei- ther peace nor con- tent- ment this

poor man could find, but a way to get rid of her came in- to his mind.

chorus

Did- dle- de- di- dil- lan- da da lan de di da did-dle do.

2. It was on a fair day morning that she gave him some "old jaw",
   So he says, "I can auction you according to the law."
   So he printed on her forehead that by auction she would go,
   And the more were the buyers the better she'd be sold.

CHORUS

3. A farmer from Kilkenny for the auction he did wait,
   With his mouth lying open like a nine-foot gate,
   He says, "Such a pretty woman I never saw before."
   And the more they bid for her, he bid a shilling more.

CHORUS

4. Now a farmer from Killarney who had just been passing by,
   He bought this old geezer at shillings twenty-five,
   Ah, she being a widow and a neighbour of his own,
   She hopped on the cart and they both drove home.

CHORUS

5. Now to conclude and finish and end upon my strife,
   This poor John Magee, he's gone home without his wife,
   May the devil follow after her, the auctioneer did say,
   And "Amen," said the women and they all joined to pray.

CHORUS

Source: *Folk Songs in Ulster*, (35). Contributed by Florence Brunnings.

Beware Young Ladies!

It is impossible to tell whether a man or a woman wrote a particular ballad, and even songs thought to be sung "by women and against men" can be taken two ways. While we might wish to think of them as pro-woman statements, telling women to make it on their own, they are also tongue-in-cheek songs which taunt women who had no real options of escape from men's designs. In other words, the message of warning would not really be taken to heart and was not a threat to men's security. "When I Was Single" and "Beware O Take Care" served a function similar to the jester in feudal courts--a temporary release from an authoritarian society. "She Is More To Be Pitied Than Censured" is a late nineteenth century dance-hall song which is unusually sympathetic to the fallen hussy. "Never Go Walking Out Without Your Hatpin" (see reference list No. 26)   jokingly warns women to defend themselves against ill-meaning rogues, but insinuates cutely that we really *do* want to be overpowered--a dangerously prevalent myth today.

Beware, O Take Care

Words and Music by Alfred Reed

This version is the one sung by Blind Alfred Reed, from West Virginia. He recorded in the late 1920's and expressed the sentiments of a man who was trying to hold onto the traditional values about women in a time of bobbed hair and flappers; witness other songs of his called "Why Do You Bob Your Hair, Girls?" and "Woman's Been After Man Ever Since."

We know young men are bold and free. Be- ware o take care. They'll tell you they're

friends, but they're liars you see. Be- ware, o take care. Be- ware young la- dies; they're

fool-ing you. Trust them not; they're fool- ing you. Be- ware young la-dies; they're fool- ing

you. Be- ware o take care! (instrumental)

2. They smoke, they chew, they wear fine shoes, beware, O take care,
   And in their pocket is a bottle of booze, beware, O take care.

CHORUS

3. Around their necks, they wear a guard, beware, O take care,
   And in their pocket is a deck of cards, beware, O take care!

CHORUS

4. They put their hands up to their hearts, they sigh, O they sigh,
   They say they love no one but you, they lie, O they lie!

CHORUS

Source: *Blind Alfred Reed* LP, Rounder 1001 (21). Also: *New Lost City Ramblers Songbook* (66).

She Is More To Be Pitied Than Censured

Traditional

This sentimental ballad appeared in the 1890's along with such greats as "Gold Will Buy Most Anything But a True Girl's Heart", "My Mother Was a Lady *or* If Jack Were Only Here", and "Take Back Your Gold." Before the advent of radio, these songs were publicized in theatres with song-slides and peddled about the town. Most of the songs about women were concerned with the continuation of the "bad girl" vs. "good girl" split which occurred when the "evils of the city" threatened to corrupt the innocent values of the country. There was a fascination for the "good girl gone bad", and this song, as well as others, shows pity and understanding but retains a condescending attitude.

Perhaps the song title "With All Her Faults I Love Her Still" sums up the attitude of the day towards the fallen women--some acceptance of the fact that she has weaknesses and is not *totally* immoral (as would be thought in some older ballads) but no insight into the causes for her wayward tendencies.

At the old con- cert hall on the Bow- ry   round a ta- ble were seat- ed   one night,

a   crowd of young fel- lows ca- rousing. With them life seemed cheer-ful and bright.

At the ver- y next ta-ble was seat- ed , a   girl who had fall- en to shame. All the

young fel-lows jeered at her down-fall, till   they heard an old wo- man ex-   plain.

"She is more to be pit- ied than cen- sured, she is more to be helped than de- spised.

She is on- ly a las- sie who ven- tured on life's storm- y path ill- ad- vised. Do not

144

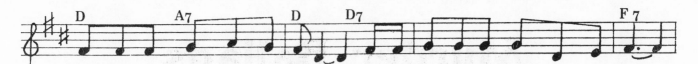

scorn her with words fierce and bit-ter. Do not laugh at her shame and down-fall.

For a mo-ment just stop and con-sid-er that a man was the cause of it all!"

2. There's an old fashioned church 'round the corner,
   Where the neighbors all gathered one day,
   While the parson was preaching a sermon
   O'er a soul who had just passed away.
   Twas the very same girl from the bowry
   Who a life of adventure had led,
   Did the clergyman jeer at her downfall?
   No, he asked for God's mercy and said:

CHORUS

Courtesy Vermont Historical Society

Reprinted from *The New Song Fest*, Ed. by Dick and Beth Best   Copyright © 1948, 1955 by R. L. Best   Used by Permission of Crown Publishers, Inc.

Source: *The New Song Fest*, p. 81, (86). Also: *Read 'Em and Weep*, p. 209, (79).

Murder Ballads

There is no need to shout "Beware!" when we see the proliferation of ballads about the murder of women. They speak for themselves. Murder ballads are a uniquely American genre, forming "more than half of ballads composed by white singers in America",[1] according to folklorist Alan Lomax. Women are favorite victims.

Nagged and insecure men and stifled and bored wives thrived on these songs which gave women "what was coming to them" for following a lover into the dark woods. They were usually not outwardly evil women, just duped innocent lovers who let up on their caution at the wrong time. Ballads were the scandal tabloids of their day. Judson Setters states:

The day of the hangin' men and boys hovered around me like bees to buy the ballet of Sampson Bush. You see, me a-bein' blind I had to earn a livin' for my family, and bein' as God gifted me with makin' song ballets I followed that. Though I don't fancy such horrible tales, it seems like most folk do. That is to say, they'll buy one about a killin' a heap quicker than a hymn tune.[2]

In those days, people learned news of the day from song ballads and not newspapers. The setting of actual murders in song pleased and informed a fascinated public. Although the words were gory and graphic in their description of the murder details, there was usually a moral tacked onto the end to justify such concern with blood and sex.

The singers (who at least in my days of collecting were predominantly respectable farm women) certainly rejoiced in the demise of their less virtuous sisters, and wagged their heads devoutly over the warning prohibitions these ballads prescribed to their sexes . . . For the people of this period, the folk ballads had a special significance; they stood for pleasure and for excitement, which the age had subordinated to work and respectability.[3]

The purity of the female victims of murder ballads almost calls to mind sacrificial offerings, which were pure and blemish-free. The murdered woman is pure, innocent and dutiful. The most popular pattern for late nineteenth and early twentieth century murder ballads has the innocent "girl" lured away to a lonely spot by her "lover" who then proceeds to murder her. This seems to be a metaphor for seduction and illicit intercourse. Lomax suggests that the murders referred to in murder ballads were a primitive form of abortion performed by a man unwilling to marry his victim.

There is also an interpretation which makes the murder ballad merely an allegory for a larger societal conflict. A sense of foreboding accompanied the growing industrial commercialism which was drawing rural America away from its origins. Rural values were idealized in the person of the virginal young woman, and the evils of the "big city" are idealized in the person of the corrupting lover.

We have included the typical variety of murder ballad--man kills woman. We refer to other types of murder ballads such as "Monongahela Sal" (woman gets her man instead of her rival), "Lord Thomas and Fair Ellinor" (woman kills her woman rival), and "The Cruel Mother" (mother kills her own children). But no matter how we count, the number of man-kills-woman ballads far outweighs the others.

[1]Alan Lomax, *Folk Songs of North America*, New York: Doubleday, 1960, p. xx.
[2]Jean Thomas, *Ballad Making in the Mountains of Kentucky*, New York: Oak, 1964, p. 138 (quote by Judson Setters).
[3]Alan Lomax, *Folk Songs of North America*, p. 80.

Wind and Rain

Traditional--As Sung by Lanayre Liggera

There are many versions of this traditional murder ballad. This particular one has the miller making fiddle pegs out of parts of the dead woman's body, and when the musical instrument is played, it sings the story of the murder. This same theme is repeated in many other known murder ballads.

The choice wasn't easy when it came to selecting murder ballads. As we stated in the introduction, over half of the recorded traditional U.S. folk songs concern murder of one sort or another, and the majority of these involved murdered women.

It was ear- ly in the month of May, oh the wind and rain. Two lov- ers went a-

fish-ing on a hot sum- mer day, cry- ing and dread- ful wind and rain.

2. He said to the lady 'Won't you marry me?"
Oh . . . rain.
"Then you my little wife will be."
Crying . . . rain.

3. She said, "Oh, no that will never do."
Oh . . . rain.
"I love you, but I can't marry you."
Crying . . . rain.

4. Then he knocked her down and he kicked her around,
Oh . . . rain.
He hit her in the head with a battering ram.
Crying . . . rain.

5. Then he threw her into the river to drown,
Oh . . . rain.
He watched her as she floated down.
Crying . . . rain.

6. She floated on down to the miller's pond,
Oh . . . rain.
Then the miller fished her out with his long fishing line.
Crying . . . rain.

7. He made fiddle pegs of her long finger bones,
Oh . . . rain.
He made fiddle pegs of her long finger bones,
Crying . . . rain.

8. He made a fiddle bow of her long curly hair,
Oh . . . rain.
He made a fiddle bow of her long curly hair,
Crying . . . rain.

9. Now the only tune that fiddle will play,
Oh the wind and the rain,
Now the only tune that fiddle will play
Is of, the dreadful wind and rain.

Source: As sung by Lanayre Liggera.

Songs of Choice

While some women passively accepted their lot in marriage and some women stayed but rebelled, other women made choices within the framework of the time. Our choices of lifestyles have always been limited, economically, socially and psychologically. Economically, there just weren't many ways for women to survive if they remained single. The factory girl really had only two choices: keep working in the factory or marry someone and work at the new job of being his wife. There was no other way for her to support herself, except as a teacher or governess or mistress (in the middle and upper class) or a maid or prostitute (in the lower class). Becoming an old maid and working at a paid job often forced her to sacrifice the support of the social structure, and if she could survive, she often did it as an outcast. Psychological limitation was a significant factor, too. It would have been difficult to make change in a vacuum. For a woman to imagine a satisfactory unmarried life was difficult when every other woman was married or trying to be. Her imagination, hence her ambition and possibility for change, was thus limited.

Today, however, there are more choices, so a traditional song of a woman making a choice may seem rather unliberated. For example, in "Wraggle-Taggle Gypsies" the woman leaves her husband to be with another man. She has chosen a very different lifestyle--that of a gypsy instead of an aristocrat--but she is still attaching herself to a man for identity. She does not choose to lead a life of adventure without a man because it would be economically unfeasible, socially unacceptable and hard for her to imagine. She has made a limited choice in the framework of our times, but a daring choice within her own. In "The House Carpenter" the woman again runs off with another man, but her fate is a warning to all listeners who consider a similar move.

"Who's Gonna Shoe Your Pretty Little Foot" (see reference list) is sometimes considered a song of a woman choosing not to be with a man at all. In some versions, the man asks who is going to do all the things she needs help with and she answers:

> Papa's gonna shoe my pretty little foot,
> Mama's gonna glove my hand.
> Sister's gonna kiss my ruby red lips,
> And I don't need no man.

She has found a way to get her needs met without him, and he is left lamenting his lost lover. If the song is sung in this version, it is quite a surprisingly feminist statement.

But other versions of the song (including the Scottish version called "Fair Annie of Lochran" and the version in *American Songbag*) have the man leaving the woman for a while, and she'll go to her family for support only until he returns. The ambiguity of the versions is a warning for us not to jump to conclusions about the progressiveness of some "feminist" ballads.

Black songs are much more open about man-woman relationships than the white ones we've dealt with, and the three Black culture songs included here all refer to choices that women have made regarding men. "I'm Going Away" simply states that the woman has had enough and is moving on. "When A Woman Blue" crystallizes the active-man, passive-woman story in a haunting way. "Wild Women Don't Worry" (see reference list) states the message of many women's blues songs of the 1920's: "If you do me wrong, I can play the same game." Blues songs seem to be more androgynous than white ballads--that is, they could be sung either by a man or a woman. Both feel the pain that comes of depending on a love relationship when they are cut off from meaningful participation in the society. We have dealt primarily with white southern folk music because we know more about it, but we can't ignore the great contributions to the American folk and blues repertoire made by black women. We feel incompetent to deal with black music in a way which would do it justice, yet to ignore it completely would be a grave omission.

Photograph by Helen McKenna

152

I'm Going Away

Words and Music by Elizabeth Cotten

Elizabeth Cotten is known for her left-handed guitar-picking technique and her other songs such as "Freight Train." She is a joy to watch in performance, and still tours around the country. This arrangement is not her original version--it would be almost impossible to get across her version without writing the guitar melody too, but listen to the record for her own special style.

The words were irresistible, however. The simple statement, "That's why I'm going away" cuts through all the usual torment of shrinkdom and indecision that we have when thinking of ending a relationship--at least in the middle class. It is the statement of a woman who is hurt, but knows enough not to stick around for more.

I'm going a- way baby, and I'm going to stay. You spends all my mon- ey. You got no

time for me. I'm going a- way honey, and I'm going to stay. Baby you're going to miss me.

That's when I go a- way. You calls me your hon- ey. You spends all my mon-ey.

Then you think that's fun- ny? That's why I'm going a- way.

2. You know you weren't true, baby, I believed in you,
   I am broken-hearted, just over the way you do.
   You said you loved me, honey, no other one but me,
   You never gave me no lovin'--that's why I'm going away.

CHORUS

3. Never gonna be no sunshine, s'gonna always be rain,
   Honey, you're gonna want me to come back again,
   Never gonna be no sunshine, s'gonna always be rain,
   You never gave me no lovin'--that's why I'm going away.

CHORUS

Source: *Shake Sugaree, Elizabeth Cotten, Vol 2 LP,* Folkways FTA 31003 (83).

When A Woman Blue

Traditional

Carl Sandburg collected this song in the 1920's. A poet named Ellis heard it in the cotton fields of Texas and performed it at the Wisconsin Players House in Milwaukee. The options for a woman who is blue are not as numerous as for a man--she couldn't "grab a railroad train and ride."

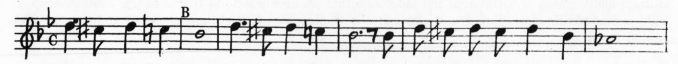

When a wo-man blue, when a wo-man blue, she hang her lit-tle head and cry.

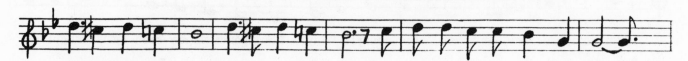

When a wo-man blue, when a wo-man blue, she hang her lit-tle head and cry.

(Hah hah hah high!) When a man get blue, he grab a rail-road train and ride.

2. I'm go'n lay my head, I'm go'n lay my head
   Down on dat railroad line--
   I'm go'n lay my head, I'm go'n lay my head,
   Down on dat railroad line--
   (Lah hah hah hine!)
   Let de train roll by,
   And dat'll pacify my min'.

Source: *American Songbag*, p. 236, (10).

Photograph by Sue Halloran

Traveling Lady

Words and Music by Rosalie Sorrels

Here's a bit of an autobiography of Rosalie Sorrels, a woman who in fact did choose to leave a life of house and family to be a traveling lady--a singer and recording artist of considerable success. Other songs that she wrote are on this album, including "She Can Do Without You."

Her book, *What, Woman, and Who, Myself, I Am* is a beautifully illustrated gem of a poem-book, songbook, quote-book and picture book examining woman's experience, and borrowing from Denise Levertov, Jean Ritchie, Dory Previn and others.

Rosalie's new album, *Always A Lady*, on Philo Records, is a statement of her life at this point and her views on children, marriage and her own self image.

I used to live in a big fine house with man-y rooms and a wide o-pen door. All of my friends used to vis-it me there, but I don't an-swer that bell an-y more.—— I used to live in a big fine house. I had room for twen-ty friends or more. Now I go beg-ging from lov-er to friend for a pal-let on an-y old floor. Oh I've got-ten to be quite a ram-bler, go-ing by land and by sea.——— Once it was a-prons and dust pans and such, but now I'm a travel-ing la-dy. and don't you try to hang on-to me.

Source: *Traveling Lady* LP, Polydor Records, Sire 5902 (95). Also: *What, Woman, and Who, Myself I Am*, (98).

2. Once it was me gave all the parties
   I baked the bread, I spread the feast, I poured the wine.
   Now I receive all my friends in a bar
   And none of these glasses are mine.
   But the bars hold notions of freedom,
   And drinking with friends or all alone.
   I find being one with the wind and the rain,
   Fogs over the visions of home.

   CHORUS

3. There's no more room to retire to,
   I've got to move, there's no place to stay,
   There's nothing that's mine but my shadow,
   And if you want that I'll give it away.

   CHORUS

Rosalie Sorrels

The House Carpenter

Traditional

This is an old ballad of European origin, also known as "James Harris" or "The Daemon Lover." In American versions, one infers the overtones of moral judgement upon her; in older European versions, the moralizing is less subtle. In Pepy's *Ballads* is the warning:

"a warning to married women, being an example of Mrs. James Reynolds (a west country woman born near Plymouth), who, having plighted her troth to a seaman, was afterwards married to a carpenter, and at last carried away by a Spirit, the manner how shall presently be recited."

In the version sung by traditional American ballad singer Almeda Riddle, the two lovers see the gates of hell, where they know they are headed. It is usually inferred that the lover is the Devil himself and not only does the erring wife die, but is condemned to eternal damnation. Enough to make women think twice about trying such an act!

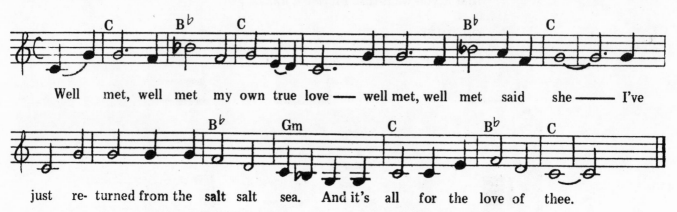

Well met, well met my own true love — well met, well met said she — I've
just re-turned from the salt salt sea. And it's all for the love of thee.

2. "Well, I could have married a king's daughter there,
And she would have married me,
But I refused the golden crown
And all for the sake of thee."

3. "If you could have married a king's daughter there,
I'm sure you are to blame;
For I am married to a house carpenter
And I think he's a nice young man."

4. "If you'll forsake your house carpenter
And come and go with me,
I'll take you where the grass grows green,
To the lands on the banks of the sea."

5. She went and picked up her sweet little babe,
And kissed it, one, two, three,
Sayin', "Stay at home with your father dear
And keep him good company."

6. She went and dressed in her very best,
As everyone could see;
She glittered and glistened and proudly she walked
The streets on the banks of the sea.

7. They hadn't been sailing but about three weeks,
I'm sure it was not four,
Till this young lady began to weep,
And her weeping never ceased any more.

8. "Are you mourning for your house carpenter?
Are you mournin' for your store?"
"No, I am mournin' for my sweet little babe
That I never will see any more."

9. They hadn't been sailing but about four weeks,
An' sure it was not more,
Till the ship spring a leak from the bottom of the sea
And it sank to rise no more.

Source: *Folk Songs of Peggy Seeger* (34). Also: *Almeda Riddle* LP, Rounder 0017 (2), (55), (11), (15), (25), (10), (36).

158

I'll Not Marry At All

Traditional--As sung by Peggy Seeger

"The theme of celibacy runs through a whole series of related and dovetailed songs which have a constant verse form in which the only variable is the designation or characteristic of the proposed mate. Sometimes the undesirable feature is particular to the man himself or his financial status (I won't marry a man that's tall, that's rich, that's old) or perhaps it's the man's profession that is the subject of all the verses (won't marry a doctor, a preacher, a lawyer, etc.); or perhaps it is something as illogical as his name (I won't marry a man named Bill, Ned, John, etc.) Occasionally the point of view is the man's or it might be a dialogue between a man and a woman, but the most common form is that printed here."

--from Peggy Seeger's introduction

The last verse sounds good to many of us today who don't want to be confined by the official doctrine of the law--but probably then, to not marry was to remain celibate unless one wished to risk the loss of respectability in the community.

I'll not mar-ry a man that's rich. He'll get drunk and fall in a ditch. And

I'll not mar-ry at all, at all. I'll not mar-ry at all, at all. I'll not mar-ry at all.

2. I'll not marry a man that's poor
   He'd have me begging from door to door,

   CHORUS

3. I'll not marry a man that's old
   His face gets wrinkled, his love gets cold,

   CHORUS

4. I'll not marry a man that's young,
   His wavering heart and perlathering tongue,

   CHORUS

5. I'll not marry a man that's fat,
   He'll just sit and kick at the cat,

   CHORUS

6. I'll not marry a man that's thin,
   He ain't nothing but bones and skin,

   CHORUS

7. I'll not marry one man at all,
   I'll stay home and favour them all.

   CHORUS

Source: *Folk Songs of Peggy Seeger*, p. 34, (37).

161

The Wraggle Taggle Gypsies

Words by Miles Wootton
Music--Traditional

There were three gyp- sies a- come to my door. And down- stairs ran this a- la- dy, O.

One sang high and the oth- er sang low. And the oth- er sang of bon- ny bon- ny

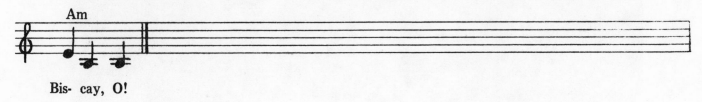

Bis- cay, O!

2. Then she pulled off her silk finished gown,
And out on hose of leather-o.
The ragged, ragged rags about our door,
And she's gone with the wraggle-taggle gypsies-o!

3. It was late last night when my lord came home,
Inquiring for his a-lady-o.
The servants said on every hand:
She's gone with the wraggle-taggle gypsies-o.

4. O, saddle me my milk-white steed,
And go fetch me my pony-o!
That I may ride and seek my bride,
Who is gone with the wraggle-taggle gypsies-o.

5. O, he rode high and he rode low,
He rode through wood and copses-o,
Until he came to a wide open field,
A-there he espied his a-lady-o.

6. What makes you leave your house and land?
What makes you leave your money-o?
What makes you leave your new-wedded lord
To go with the wraggle-taggle gypsies-o?

7. What care I for my house and land?
What care I for my money-o?
What care I for my new-wedded lord?
I'm off with the wraggle-taggle typsies-o

8. Last night you slept on a goose-feather bed,
With the sheet turned down so bravely-o!
Tonight you'll sleep in a cold, open field,
Along with the wraggle-taggle gypsies-o!

9. What care I for a goose-feather bed,
With the sheet turned down so bravely-o!
For tonight I shall sleep in a coid, open field,
Along with the wraggle-taggle gypsies-o!

Source: *Liberated Woman's Songbook*, p. 110, (93). Also: *Songs for Swingin' Housemothers* (88).

At a folk music concert for the Boston Folk Song Society, Frankie Armstrong sang the following updated parody of this song:

The Hippies and the Beatniks - new words by Miles Wooton, used by permission.

1. Rather late last night Mr. Jones came home, on the 8:45 from Victoria, O
   He was rich and fat with a big bowler hat,
   And he hated the hippies and the beatniks-o.

2. Well, he stuck his key in his mock Tudor door,
   And he cried to his wife, "I'm home, dear-o,
   The train was late and I had to wait,
   It must have been the hippies and the beatniks-o."

3. No answer came as he stepped inside,
   But his daughter came down to meet him-o,
   Crying "Mummy's not here--she's gone I fear
   Away with the hippies and the beatniks-o."

4. "Oh fill up the tank of the four-litre Jag,
   For the Mini is not so speedy-o,
   And I will drive till I find her alive
   Or dead with the hippies and the beatniks-o."

5. So he drove high and he drove low,
   Down motorways and highways too,
   Till he came soon to a hippie commune,
   And there he espied Mrs. Jones-o.

6. "What makes you leave your house and car,
   Your washing machine and tele-o,
   Your children three--not to mention me
   To go with the hippies and the beatniks-o?"

7. "Oh, what care I for my house and car,
   My washing machine and tele-o,
   My children three--for now I am free
   To go with the hippies and the beatniks-o."

8. "And as for you--well the day I rue
   That ever we got married-o,
   I'll grow my hair and I'll travel anywhere
   Along with the hippies and the beatniks-o!"

   ———————

Some stories are timeless!

Adventurous Women and Tricksters

It's refreshing to hear a song of a bold, adventurous female in the midst of numerous passive role models. But such deviants were few, especially in American folklore. However, some gems of song exist in the British folk tradition. One of them, "The Crafty Maid's Policy" (and its American variant, "Broomfield Hill") still makes the women in the audience chuckle with vengeance. Women-in-men's-clothing songs, such as "Tarry Trousers" and "The Handsome Cabin Boy" are also liked by audiences with a feminist consciousness, even though the woman usually dresses up to be with a lover on board a ship or on the battlefield. In some rare songs, women dress as men just for the fun of it, and don't follow any mate. But even in these tales, there is the suggestion that these songs were motivated more by male fantasy than by the wish to portray strong females:

. . . the dream that one of their companions might be a girl dressed as a boy is an inevitable fantasy for lonely men in barrack and bunk and fo'c'sle hammock.[1]

[1]A. L. Lloyd, *Folk Song in England*, New York: International Publishing Co., 1968, p. 226.

Courtesy Vermont Historical Society

The Crafty Maid's Policy

Traditional-As sung by Frankie Armstrong

There are many good songs of this trickster genre. One other story goes that the woman is in the country alone, and escapes by telling her attacker (suitor?) that she is willing, but that it isn't a good time: he should meet her at such and such a place and time. He agrees and leaves, she escapes to safety.

The song "The Crafty Maid's Policy" has been found in an 1860 broadside in London, printed by Disley of St. Giles. Frankie Armstrong has been singing songs of liberated women for years, and on the record listed above there are many beautiful traditional songs of strong women. She also sings, on the record *Female Frolic* (along with Peggy Seeger and Sandra Kerr), more songs of this type.

Come lis- ten a- while and I'll sing you a song, of three mer- ry gen- tle- men rid- ing

a - long. They met a fair maid and to her did say, "We're a- fraid this cold morn-ing will

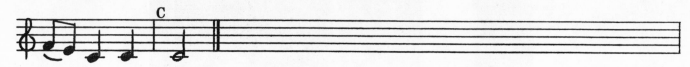

do you some harm."

2. "Oh, no, kind sir," said the maid, "you're mistaken,
   To think this cold morning would do me some harm.
   There's one thing I crave; it lies twixt your legs.
   If you give me that it will keep me warm."

3. "Then since you do crave it, my dear you shall have it,
   If you come with me to yonder green tree.
   Then since you do crave it, my dear you shall have it.
   I'll make these two gentlemen witness to be."

4. So the gentleman lighted, and straightway she mounted
   And looking the gentleman hard in the face, saying
   "You knew not me meaning, you wrong understood me,"
   And away she went galloping down the long lane.

5. "Oh gentlemen lend me one of your horses,
   That I may ride after her down the long lane.
   If I overtake her, I warrant I'll make her
   Return unto me my own horse again."

Source: *Lovely on the Water* LP, Topic Records 12TS216 (59).

166

6. But soon as this fair maid she saw him a-coming,
   She instantly then took her pistol in hand, saying
   "Doubt not my skill; it's you I would kill.
   I'd have you stand back or you were a dead man."

7. "Oh, why do you spend your time here in talking,
   Oh why do you spend your time here in vain?
   Come, give her a guinea, it's what she deserves and I
   Warrant she'll give you your horse back again."

8. "Oh, no, kind sir, you're vastly mistaken.
   If it is his loss, well, it is my gain,
   And you were a witness that he give it to me."
   And away she went galloping over the plain.

The Handsome Cabin Boy

Traditional

This is one of the many traditional women-in-men's-clothing songs. Even though her independence was such that "her mind was bent on ramblin' ", not simply following her lover somewhere, she still ends up with a baby. The beginning of her mother days are the end of her sailor days--and we never hear how she feels about this abrupt end to her adventure!

'Tis of a hand-some fe- male, as you may un-der-stand. Her mind being bent on

ram-bl- ing un- to some for- eign land. She dressed her self in Sail-or's clothes or so it

does ap-pear,_____ and hired with our cap- tain to serve him for a year.

2. The captain's wife she being on board, she seemed in great joy,
   To see her husband had engaged such a handsome cabin boy.
   And now and then she'd slip in a kiss, and she would have like to toy,
   But it was the captain found out the secret of the handsome cabin boy.

3. His cheeks were red and rosy and his hair hung in its curls,
   The sailors often smiled and said he looks just like a girl.
   But eating the captain's biscuits, their color didn't destroy,
   And the waist did swell on pretty Nell, the handsome cabin boy.

4. 'Twas in the Bay of Biscay our gallant ship did plow,
   One night among the sailors was a fearful scurrying row.
   They tumbled from their hammocks, for their sleep it did destroy,
   And swore about the groaning of the handsome cabin boy.

Source: *The Liberated Woman's Songbook*, p. 114 (93).

5. "Oh, doctor, dear doctor," the cabin boy did cry,
   "My time has come, I am undone and I must surely die."
   The doctor come a-running and he smiled at the fun,
   To think a sailor lad should have a daughter or a son.

6. The sailors, when they heard the joke, they all did stand and stare,
   The child belonged to none of them, they solemnly did swear,
   The captain's wife she looked at him and said, "I wish you joy,
   For it's either you or I betrayed the handsome cabin boy."

7. Then each man took his tot of rum, and drunk success to trade,
   And likewise to the cabin boy, who was neither man nor maid.
   Here's hoping the wars don't rise again, our sailors to destroy,
   And here's hoping for a jolly lot more like the handsome cabin boy.

Tarry Trousers

Traditional--As Sung by Frankie Armstrong

This mother-daughter dialogue is a common folk theme. This version is probably less than 200 years old, and is known from Yorkshire to Somerset, England. Dickens knew the song and he makes Captain Cuttle sing a scrap of it in *Donley & Son*. This version is substantially the one sung to Vaughn Williams by Mrs. Humphreys of Ingrave.

She follows her lover into battle (or would like) and even takes to cheering on the soldiers in a very sporting fashion.

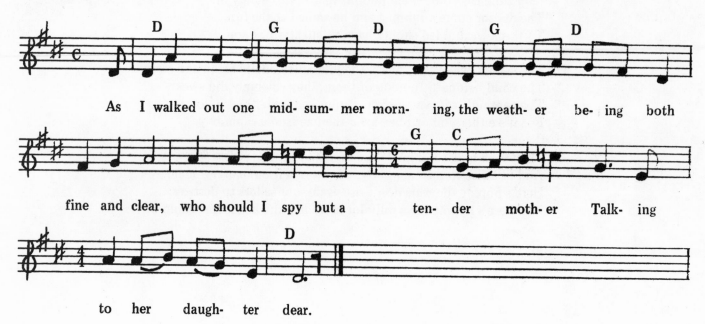

As I walked out one mid-sum-mer morn- ing, the weath-er be- ing both fine and clear, who should I spy but a ten- der moth- er Talk- ing to her daugh- ter dear.

2. "Daughter, I would have you marry and live no more a single life."
   But she says, "Mother, I'd rather tarry for my sailor boy so bright."

3. "But, daughter, they are giv'n to roamin', into foreign countries they do go,
   And then they'll leave you broken hearted, and that will prove your overthrow."

4. "I'll dress myself in sailor's clothing, no foreign dangers will I fear,
   And when I'm in the height of battle then I'll protect my Jamie dear."

5. "Hark how the big guns they do rattle and the small guns they do make their noise,
   And when I'm in the height of battle I'll yell 'Fight on, me jolly boys!'"

6. "Me mother would have me wed a tailor and rob me of me heart's delight,
   But give me the lad whose tarry trousers shine to me like diamonds bright.

Source: *Lovely On the Water* LP, Topic Records 12TS216 (59).

170

Women and Work

The past (as well as the present) stereotype of woman as wife and mother ignores the fact that many women had to work for wages. Some chose to work and remain independent for awhile (such as the middle-class textile workers in New England). Others were forced into working under deplorable conditions for low wages when their husbands were disabled and their children were hungry. Work outside the home in textile mills was very common for women in the late nineteenth century, and "Southern Cotton Mill Rhyme" expresses the worries of a working class woman of the time. "Hustlin' Blues" concerns "the oldest profession in the world" for women.

"Work" is used here both traditionally and in a new way. As the wages-for-housework movement gains attention, we are forced to regard housework as a job, whether it is paid or not. "Housewife's Lament" is a virtual job-description of work at home.

Whether in the home or in the factory, 1830's or 1970's, the oppression of working women did, and still does, reflect the plight of workers who have not yet achieved control over the products of their labor.

Photograph by Elsa Dorfman

Southern Cotton Mill Rhyme

Traditional--As sung by Roy Berkeley

In 1930, *New Masses* (a U.S. leftist publication) printed "Southern Cotton Mill Rhyme", collected by Grace Lumpkin at a National Textile Workers hall in Charlotte, North Carolina. It was composed years before by an anonymous mill weaver in Buffalo, South Carolina to the tune of "John Hardy" or "Warren Harding's Widow." When it was sung in 1929, the lyrics were changed from "when the day of judgement comes" to "when the Great Revolution comes"--a political and not a religious fate for the oppressors! Either way, it expresses the feelings of an overworked woman who can't live up to the middle-class ideals of beauty, and knows who her oppressors are.

I was born way down south in the town of Buf-fa-lo. Worked in the

mills with re rest of the trash, as we're of-ten called, you know.

2. You factory folks who hear my song will surely understand,
   The reason why I love you so, is that I'm a factory hand.

3. We work all day, we work real hard, and toil from soon to late,
   We have no time to primp and fuss, or to dress right up to date.

4. And our children, they grow up learned, no time to go to school,
   Almost before they have learned to walk, they have learned to spin and spool.

5. Foreman jerks them round and round, and whistles mighty keen,
   I'll tell you what--those factory kids are really treated mean.

6. The fancy folks who live in town and spend their money free
   Will hardly talk to a factory hand that dresses like you and me.

7. 'Cause we go walking down the street, all covered with lint and strings,
   They call us fools and factory trash, and other low-down things.

8. Well let them wear their watches fine, their rings and pearly strings,
   When the day of judgement comes, we'll make them shed their pretty things.

Source: Heard in concert by Roy Berkeley, Indian Neck, Conn., 1974. Also: *The Working Girl* LP,
Voyager Records 3055 (94).

Photograph by Jane Melnick

Hustlin' Blues

Words and Music by Ma Rainey

Ma Rainey was called "The Mother of the Blues." Her career began in the Black vaudeville circuits around the turn of the century. She was a great classic blues singer (see introduction to "Wild Women Don't Worry" by Ida Cox for more about classic blues). "Hustlin' Blues" embodies a "worker's struggle" as intense and long-enduring as society itself, in "the oldest profession."

It's rain-in' out here and the tricks ain't walk-in to- night. It's rain-in' out here and the tricks ain't walk-in' to- night. I'm go-in' home. I know I've got to fight.

2. If you hits me tonight let me tell you what I'm goin' to do,
   If you hits me tonight let me tell you what I'm goin' to do,
   I'm gonna take you to a court and tell the judge on you.

3. I ain't made no money and he dared me to go home,
   I ain't made no money and he dared me to go home,
   Judge I told him he'd better leave me alone.

4. He followed me up and he grabbed me for a fight,
   He followed me up and he grabbed me for a fight,
   He said, "Gal, do you know you ain't made no money tonight?"

5. Oh, judge, tell him I'm through,
   Oh, judge, tell him I'm through,
   I'm tired of this life, that's why I brought him to you.

Ma Rainey can be heard on Biograph Record BLP 12011, 12001, 12032.   Used by Permission

Source: *Oh My Babe Blues* LP, Biograph Records 12011 (69).

Oh, hard is the fortune
Of all womankind.
They're always controlled
They're always confined
Controlled by their parents
Until they are wives
And slaves to their husbands
The rest of their lives.

traditionalballad

Housewife's Lament

Traditional

"You had to be a stout body to be a woman way up west in the Ohio wilderness," said one old lady, who had raised a big crop of children and grandchildren. "There wasn't no time to get out side the clearin'. Squash, pumpkins, potatoes, beans, beets, turnips and the rest of the garden truck to be planted, hoed, and gathered. Made our own candles and spun our own flax and wool. The man of the house would go off hunting and git a deer or two, and then laze around between crops. But we never got away from the spinning wheel, the cooking fire and the baby's cradle. I remember a neighbor lady who picked up her knitting and knitted a few rounds at her own husband's funeral, she was so used to keeping busy the whole time."

--from *Folk Songs of North America*, p. 124.

This song was found in the diary of Sarah Price of Ottowa, Illinois. Sarah raised seven sons and lived to see them die in the Civil War. The song may have been composed for some comic presentation--it has been found in other parts of the country--but by putting it in her diary, she must have felt it was her song.

A friend of ours taught guitar to a 13-year-old girl from Boston, who wrote her own version of the last verse:

But when I awoke and found it was over,
I threw down my broom and I ran towards the door,
Reaching outside, I cast off my apron,
And swore I would never clean house anymore.

Let's hope there's more young women around like Lydia Snow, who wrote this version!

From *Folk Songs of North America*, ed. by Alan Lomax. Collected by John Lomas; recorded and arranged by Alan Lomax; New York: Doubleday, 1960. Used by Permission

Source: *The Liberated Woman's Songbook*, p. 34 (93). Also: *Folksongs of North America* (36), *Virgo Rising* LP (97), (50), (91).

prices they dou-ble, and no-thing is as I would wish it to be!"

(repeat chorus after every verse)

2. "There's too much of worriment goes in a bonnet,
   There's too much of ironing goes in a shirt,
   There's nothing that's worth all the time you waste on it,
   There's nothing that lasts us but trouble and dirt.

3. "In March it is mud, it is slush in December,
   The midsummer breezes are loaded with dust,
   In fall the leaves litter, in muddy September
   The wallpaper rots and the candlesticks rust.

4. "There are worms in the cherries and slugs on the roses
   And ants in the sugar and mice in the pies,
   The rubbish of spiders no mortal supposes,
   And ravaging roaches and damaging flies.

5. "It's sweeping at six and it's dusting at seven,
   It's victuals at eight and it's dishes at nine,
   It's potting and panning from ten to eleven,
   We scarce break our fast till we plan how to dine.

6. "With grease and with grime, from corner to center
   Forever at war and forever alert,
   No rest for a day lest the enemy enter,
   I spend my whole life in a struggle with dirt!

7. "Last night in my dreams I was stationed forever
   On a far little rock in the midst of the sea,
   My one chance of life was a ceaseless endeavor
   To sweep off the waves as they swept over me!

8. "Alas, 'twas no dream--ahead I behold it,
   I see I am helpless my fate to avert."
   She lay down her broom, her apron she folded.
   She lay down and died and was buried in dirt.

Photograph by Earl Dotter

Women in Struggle

In the 1930's, a few American southern women played a vital musical role in the organizing attempts in both the coal and textile mines. Aunt Molly Jackson and Sarah Ogan Gunning both sang songs of their real experiences among the poor coal miners who were striking. Aunt Molly was the sister, daughter and wife of a miner, and though her songs are not specifically for a raise in her own wages, her reasons for singing were her concerns as a woman for her dying children. A woman's song about a men's strike, but still a woman's song. Florence Reese wrote "Which Side Are You On?" during a coal miners' strike in the 1930's and Ella May Wiggins who wrote "Mill Mother's Lament" about her experiences working in the cotton mills, was shot to death as she rode in a truck at a union rally. For these women, the strikes were a question of survival, not an abstract political issue. Other women who used and still use song in their political struggles are Sis Cunningham, a founder of *Broadside* magazine and an ex-Almanac singer, Kathy Kahn, who works today with organizing the poor in Appalachia, and Hedy West, who is known for her traditional song repertoire and organizing work in the South along with her father, Don West.

The last two songs, "Bread and Roses" and "Let Us All Speak Our Minds" are songs arising from the first women's struggle in this country. They are the closest cousins to today's feminist songs and laid the groundwork for the women's consciousness which is flowering today.

Several of the songs in this section were written by women who struggled along side their husbands, brothers, and fathers through the 1930's Harlan County, Ky. unionizing battles between the coal miners and the companies with their hired gun thugs. Tragicly, these songs are still appropriate today.

The pictures accompanying these songs were taken during the summer of 1973 when the Brookside miners in Harlan County voted to be represented by the United Mine Workers rather than the Southern Labor Union (a union notorious in Appalachia as being company dominated.) The Duke Power Company who owns the Brookside mine refused to negotiate with the UMW. The miners went out on strike in July and all hell broke loose. Legal justice is scarce in Harlan County where the judge, himself, is a coal operator. Duke Power acquired court injunctions against picketing, and many of the miners ended up in jail.

Without a strong picket line to keep out scabs recruited from the impoverished hills with the promise of huge daily wages, the miners would be powerless. Since the miners couldn't picket, the women and children did. Women carrying brooms and mops marched the picket line, carrying on the struggle between Appalachian poverty and the giant multi-million dollar corporations. Eventually, many of these women were also jailed.

This was the beginning of the Brookside Women's Club. The women met weekly and continued to support the strike in a number of ways. They womaned the picket lines, raised money, publicized and organized support for the strike throughout Appalachia, and eventually throughout the country. When the Brookside strike was finally settled in the miners' favor over a year later, the women decided to keep meeting, and to travel throughout Appalachia, organizing other women to form their own "Women's Clubs."

(Many thanks to Earl Dotter for providing us with photos and to Angie Sherbo for providing information.)

Aunt Molly Sings Old-Time Songs

Here is pipe-smoking Aunt Molly Jackson, of Southeastern Kentucky, a ballad singer who is pictured leading a group of folk culture students in New York University in singing one of her own compositions. Aunt Molly, making her appearances "up north" to raise funds for the coal miners in this section, has made a hit with the students, with hertales of the mountains an dher tobacco-chewing days.

Coal Wage Differential Contested By Operators

Knoxville, Tenn.—This district of business and principal coal petition is given any further advantage in wage scale, it was announced last night following the fact that a wage settlement in the Alabama district between operators which provides a more favorable settlement for that field than has been given in the South

I Am A Union Woman

This song is also known as "Join the C.I.O." or "Join the N.M.U." It was originally written as "Join the N.M.U." in the 1930's and later changed to "Join the C.I.O." We have left it in the original version as a tribute to the first organization.

Aunt Molly Jackson was a coal miner's daughter, wife and mother who helped organize the Appalachian miners in the bloody, violent 1930's. She was rooted in the traditional singing style of unaccompanied church singing, as was her half-sister, Sarah Ogan Gunning. The songs she wrote, after losing a husband, brother and son, tell her bitter stories. She died in obscurity in California in 1961.

More of her songs are available on the Rounder album listed below and on *The Songs and Stories of Aunt Molly Jackson*, Folkways FH 5457.

I am a un-ion wo-man, just as brave as I can be. I do not like the boss-es

and the boss-es don't like me. Join the N. M. U. Come join the N. M. U.

2. I was raised in old Kentucky
   In Kentucky born and bred,
   And when I joined the union
   They called me a Rooshian Red.

CHORUS

3. This is the worst time on earth
   That I have ever saw,
   To get killed out by gun thugs
   And framed up by the law.

CHORUS

4. When my husband asked the boss for a job,
   This is the words he said:
   "Bill Jackson, I can't work you, sir,
   Your wife's a Rooshian Red."

CHORUS

5. If you want to join a union,
   As strong as one can be,
   Join the dear old NMU,
   And come along with me.

CHORUS

6. We are many thousand strong
   And I am glad to say,
   We are getting stronger
   And stronger every day.

CHORUS

7. If you want to get your freedom,
   Also your liberty,
   Join the dear old NMU,
   Also the I.L.D.

CHORUS

8. The bosses ride big fine horses,
   While we walk in the mud.
   Their banner is the dollar sign,
   While ours is striped with blood.

CHORUS

Source: *The Liberated Woman's Songbook*, p. 72 (93). Also: *Aunt Molly Jackson* LP, Rounder 1002 (13), *Hard-Hitting Songs for Hard Hit People*, p. 142 (43), (87).

I Hate The Company Bosses

Moses Asch of Folkways Records first heard Sarah sing this song in 1939 and said it was the most radical composition he had ever heard. The original title was "I Hate the Capitalist System," but Sarah later changed it because folks thought it was too radical. But for her it was a personal statement, not rhetoric. Her loved ones really had died, due to the terrible conditions in the coal mines. The tune is related to two tunes known in mountain tradition: the Carter Family melody for "The Sailor Boy" (Laws K12) and "On the Banks of that Lonely River", collected by Combs from his mother's singing on Troublesome Creek, Knott County, Ky.

This song comes from a group of militant songs put to old melodies which were written during the 1930's in the coal areas of the Southern highlands. Both Sarah and her half-sister Aunt Molly Jackson were well-versed in traditional songs, and used their talents and experience as miners' daughters, sisters and wives to produce these songs. Sarah's family was blacklisted from the mines for their organizing activities, and only the intervention of Elizabeth Barnicle, folklorist from the North, saved her from starving to death. She moved north and was acclaimed by the folksong "revival" people such as Pete Seeger and Woody Guthrie. Since then she has been appearing at festivals, the most recent of which was the Down East Festival at Tufts University in 1974.

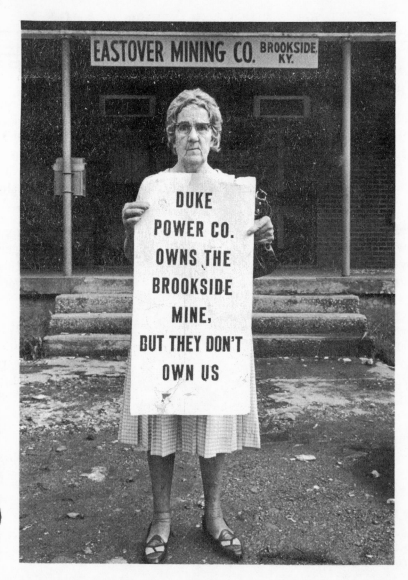

Photograph by Earl Dotter

I Hate The Company Bosses

Words and Music by Sarah Ogan Gunning

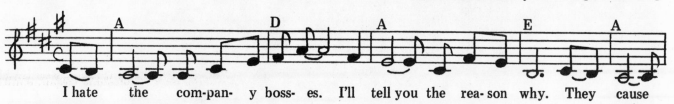

I hate the com-pan-y boss-es. I'll tell you the rea-son why. They cause

me so much suf-fering and my dear-est friends to die.

2. Oh yes, I guess you wonder
   What they have done to me.
   I'm going to tell you, mister,
   My husband had T.B.

3. Brought on by hard work and low wages
   And not enough to eat,
   Going naked and hungry,
   No shoes upon his feet.

4. I guess you'll say he's lazy
   And did not want to work.
   But I must say you're crazy,
   For work he did not shirk.

5. My husband was a coal miner,
   He worked and risked his life
   To try to support three children,
   Himself, his mother, and wife.

6. I had a blue-eyed baby,
   The darling of my heart.
   But from my little darling
   Her mother had to part.

7. These mighty company bosses,
   They dress in jewels and silk.
   But my darling blue-eyed baby,
   She starved to death for milk.

8. I had a darling mother,
   For her I often cry.
   But with them rotten conditions
   My mother had to die.

9. Well, what killed your mother?
   I heard these bosses say.
   Dead of hard work and starvation,
   My mother had to pay.

10. Well, what killed your mother?
    Oh tell us, if you please.
    Excuse me, it was pellagra,
    That starvation disease.

11. They call this the land of plenty,
    To them I guess it's true.
    But that's to the company bosses,
    Not workers like me and you.

12. Well, what can I do about it,
    To these men of power and might?
    I tell you, company bosses,
    I'm going to fight, fight, fight.

13. What can we do about it,
    To right this dreadful wrong?
    We're all going to join the union,
    For the union makes us strong.

Source: *Sarah Ogan Gunning* LP, Folk Legacy FSA-26 (82). Also: *Hard-Hitting Songs for Hard Hit People*, p. 164 (43), (94).

Which Side Are You On?

Words by Florence Reece
Music--Traditional

In the spring of 1931 the coal miners of Harlan County, Kentucky, were on strike, along with thousands of other members of the National Miners' Union throughout the country. The company gun thugs went around the countryside, terrorizing the organizers, miners and families. Florence's husband Sam was an organizer, and one day she tore an old calendar off the wall and wrote the words of the song. Then she and her daughter put it to the tune of an old hardshell Baptist hymn.

--from *People's Songs*, Vol. 2, No. 1

The J.H. Blair referred to was John Henry Blair, who was High Sheriff of Harlan County and just happened to be a part-owner of the mine!

Come all of you good work-ers. Good news to you I'll tell, of how the good old un- ion

has come in here to dwell. Which side are you on? Which side are you on?

2. Don't scab for the bosses,
Don't listen to their lies.
Us poor folks haven't got a chance
Unless we organize.

CHORUS

3. They say in Harlan County
There are no neutrals there.
You'll either be a union man
Or a thug for J. H. Blair.

CHORUS

4. Oh, workers can you stand it?
Oh, tell me how you can.
Will you be a lousy scab,
Or will you be a man?

CHORUS

5. My daddy was a miner,
And I'm a miner's son;
And I'll stick with the union
Till every battle's won.

CHORUS

Photograph by Jane Melnick

Bread and Roses

Words by James Oppenheim
Music by Caroline Kohlsaat

The Massachusetts state legislature, in its closing session of 1911, passed a law limiting hours of children under eighteen to 54 hours a week. The textile corporations, in retaliation for this worker victory, cut all employee hours to 54 per week, with wages cut correspondingly. The workers in the Lawrence, Mass. textile mills began a nine week strike, January 1, 1912. Women workers carried banners: "Bread and Roses" in their walkout marches. Just as in the family, where women had the role of keeper of morals and upholder of beauty, the women fought not only for workers' rights but for the quality of life.

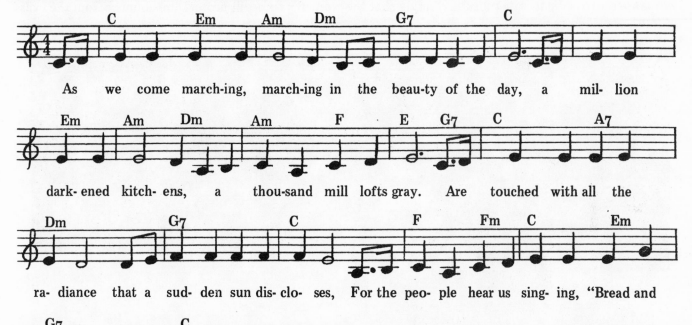

As we come march-ing, march-ing in the beau-ty of the day, a mil-lion dark-ened kitch-ens, a thou-sand mill lofts gray. Are touched with all the ra-diance that a sud-den sun dis-clo-ses, For the peo-ple hear us sing-ing, "Bread and

Ros-es, Bread and Ros-es."

2. As we come marching, marching, we battle too, for men,
For they are women's children and we mother them again.
Our lives shall not be sweated from birth until life closes,
Hearts starve as well as bodies:
Give us bread but give us roses.

3. As we come marching, marching, unnumbered women dead
Go crying through our singing their ancient songs of bread.
Small art and love and beauty their drudging spirits knew.
Yest, it is bread that we fight for,
But we fight for roses, too.

4. As we come marching, marching, we bring the Greater Days,
The rising of the women means the rising of the race.
No more the drudge and idler, ten that toil where one reposes,
But a sharing of life's glories,
Bread and Roses, Bread and Roses.

Reprinted from *Songs of Work and Freedom* by Edith Fowke and Joe Glazer   Used by Permission

Source: *Songs of Work and Freedom* (91). Also: *The Liberated Woman's Songbook*, p. 60 (93), *Honor Thy Womanself* LP, Rounder 4006 (48).

Let Us All Speak Our Minds

"The songs of women's independence were both applauded and hissed during America's coming of age, but none received more defiant approval or contempt than the song of the militant feminist, "Let Us All Speak Our Minds,"--from *Songs of Yesterday*, Doubleday Doran, New York, 1941, quoted in Philip D. Jordan's notes to the Folkways album.

This is one of the more interesting songs to come out of the singing suffrage movement. Most of the words are set to old patriotic tunes, and imply that the women's vote will protect the country from the evils of immigrants' voting!

Photograph by Jane Melnick

Source: *The Liberated Woman's Songbook*, p. 54 (93). Also: *Songs of the Suffragettes* LP, Folkways 5281 (90), (91).

Let Us All Speak Our Minds

Words by William Brough
Music by J. G. Maeder

Men tell us it's fit that wives should sub- mit to their hus- bands sub- mis- siv- ly weak-ly;

Tho' what- ev- er they say, their wives should o- bey, un- ques- tion- ing, stu-pid- ly, meek-ly.

Our hus- bands would make us their own dic- tum take, with- out ev- er a where-fore or

why for it. But I don't and I can't and I won't and I shan't; No I will speak my mind if

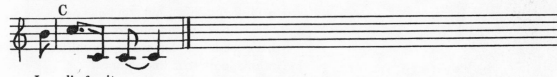

I die for it.

2. For we know it's all fudge to say man's the best judge
Of what should be and shouldn't, and so on.
That woman should bow, nor attempt to say how
She considers that matters should go on.
I never yet gave up myself thus a slave,
However my husband might try for it;
For I can't and I won't and I sha'n't and I don't,
But I will speak my mind if I die for it.

3. And all ladies I hope who've with husbands to cope,
With the rights of the sex will not trifle.
We all, if we choose, our tongues but to use,
Can all opposition soon stifle.
Let man, if he will, then bid us be still
And silent, a price he'll pay high for it.
For we won't and we can't and we don't and we sha'n't,
Let us all speak our minds if we die for it.

Dreadful Memories

Words by Sarah Ogan Gunning and Aunt Molly Jackson
Music--Traditional

The melody for this song comes from the hymn "Precious Memories" but both Sarah and Aunt Molly Jackson had only "Dreadful Memories" and told it that way. In 1952, John Greenway visited Aunt Molly in Sacramento and she said she wrote it in 1935 about an experience that happened in 1931. Sarah sang it in 1963 for Archie Green and said she wrote it and taught it to Aunt Molly during World War II. The two sisters' versions are somewhat different, and are within a single family tradition; the experiences were certainly common to them both.

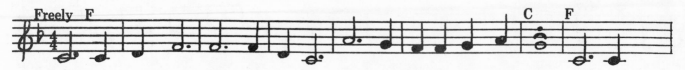

Dread- ful mem-ories, how they lin- ger. How they ev-er flood my soul. How the

work- ers and their child-ren die from hun- ger and from cold.

Sarah Ogan Gunning

2. Hungry fathers, wearied mothers
   Living in those dreadful shacks,
   Little children cold and hungry
   With no clothing on their backs.

3. Dreadful gun-thugs and stool-pigeons
   Always flock around our door.
   What's the crime that we've committed?
   Nothing, only that we're poor.

4. When I think of all the heartaches
   And all the things that we've been through,
   Then I wonder how much longer
   And what a working man can do.

5. Really, friends, it doesn't matter
   Whether you are black or white.
   The only way you'll ever change things
   Is to fight and fight and fight.

6. We will have to join the union,
   They will help you find a way
   How to get a better living
   And for your work get better pay.

Source: *Sarah Ogan Gunning: Girl of Constant Sorrow* LP, Folk Legacy FSA-26 (82). Also: *American Industrial Folksongs* LP, Riverside 12-607 (8), *The Songs and Stories of Aunt Molly Jackson* LP, Folkways 5457 (87), (94).

Other Songs In Each Category

Numbered Reference List

1. A Tribute to Woody Guthrie, Part Two, record, Folkways 2586.
2. Almeda Riddle, record, Rounder 0017. General traditional material.
3. American Ballads and Folk Songs, ed. by John and Alan Lomax. New York: Macmillan, 1943.
4. American Favorite Ballads, record, Folkways FA2323, Vol. 4.
5. American Favorite Ballads, ed. by Pete Seeger. New York: Oak, 1961.
6. American Favorite Ballads Sung by Pete Seeger, record, Folkways FT 1017.
7. American Folksongs of Protest, by John Greenway. University of Pennsylvania Press, Philadelphia, 1953.
8. American Industrial Folksongs, record, Riverside 12-607.
9. American Murder Ballads, by Olive Burt. New York: Oxford Press, 1968.
10. American Songbag, ed. by Carl Sandburg. New York: Harcourt, Brace & World, 1927.
11. Anthology of American Folk Music, ed. by Ethel Raim and Josh Dunson. New York: Oak, 1972.
12. At This Present Moment, record, Rounder 4003. Topical songs set to traditional-sounding melodies. Lyrics concern U.S. imperialism, education, women's issues. By Peggy Seeger and Ewan McColl.
13. Aunt Molly Jackson, record, Rounder 1002. Songs and stories by Aunt Molly herself.
14. Babies in the Mill, record, Testament 3301. Sung by Nancy and Dorsey Dixon. Songs about women and children working in the textile mills.
15. Ballad Book, ed. by John Jacob Niles. Boston: Houghton Mifflin Co., 1961.
16. Ballad Making in the Mountains of Kentucky, by Jean Thomas. New York: Oak, 1964.
17. Bergerfolk: Happy Landings, record, Folkways FTS32416.
18. Berkeley Women's Music Collective Songbook, order from The Women's Press Collective, 5251 Broadway, Oakland, CA 94618.
19. Best of Dolly Parton, record, RCA Victor 4449.
20. Big Star Falling Mama, by Hettie Jones. New York: Viking Press, 1974. The lives of five black women singers.
21. Blind Alfred Reed, record, Rounder 1001. "How Can A Poor Man Stand Such Times and Live" record contains many songs of the mores of the depression years--songs of bobbed hair, nagging wives, written or arranged by Blind Alfred Reed.
22. But The Women Rose, record, Folkways FC5536. A two-record set of significant speeches in the women's movement.
23. Celebration of Life, songbook by Jean Ritchie. Pictures and reminiscences of Jean Ritchie's life in the southern mountains, original songs and arrangements.
24. Come from the Shadows, record, A&M S4339. Sung and written by Joan Baez. Songs of political and personal struggles.
25. Eighty English Folk Songs from the Southern Appalachians, ed. by Cecil Sharp and Maud Karpeles. Cambridge, Mass.: MIT Press, 1968.
26. Elsa Lanchester Sings Bawdy Ballads, record, Everest Records (10920 Wilshire Blvd., Los Angeles, CA 90024). Some tongue-in-cheek bawdy ballads "for women"--not feminist but historically fascinating.
27. English Dance and Song, magazine. Spring 1972, Vol. 14, No. 1 (2 Regents Park Rd., London).
28. Famous Original Hits by 25 Great Country Music Artists, record, Country Hall of Fame, Beverly Hills, CA.
29. Female Frolic, record, Argo 82 (out of print). With Peggy Seeger, Frankie Armstrong and Sandra Kerr. Songs of adventurous women, women and work, from English tradition.
30. Flat-Picker's Guitar Guide, by Jerry Silverman. New York: Oak, 1963.
31. Folk Ballads of the English Speaking World, record, Folkways FA2310.
32. Folk Singer's Guitar Guide, by Jerry Silverman. New York: Oak, 1973.
33. Folk Song Today, magazine, ed. by Tony Wales, No. 4. English Folk and Dance Society Publications Ltd. (50 New Bond St., London, WI).
34. Folk Song U.S.A. (Best Known American Folk Songs), ed. by John and Alan Lomax, New York: Duell, Sloan and Pearce, Inc., 1947.
35. Folk Songs in Ulster, ed. by Robin Morton. Cork: Mercier Press, 1970.
36. Folk Songs of North America, ed. by Alan Lomax. New York: Doubleday, 1960.
37. Folksongs of Peggy Seeger, ed. by Peggy Seeger. New York: Oak, 1964.
38. Folksongs of Vermont, record, Folkways FH5314. Sung by Margaret MacArthur.
39. Force of Life, record, Paredon P--1023. Radical contemporary songs by the Red Star Singers of California.
40. Frank Wakefield with Country Cooking, record, Rounder 0007.
41. Guitar Finger-Picking Styles, by Happy Traum. New York: Oak, 1966.
42. Hang In There, Redwood Records. Songs by Holly Near about her contacts with people through the FTA Southeast Asia tours and the Indo-China Peace Campaign.
43. Hard Hitting Songs for Hard Hit People, ed. by Alan Lomax, Pete Seeger and Woody Guthrie. New York: Oak, 1966.
44. Harps in the Wind, by Carol Brinks. New York: MacMillan, 1947. The story of the singing Hutchinson family of New England, who sang for abolition of slavery, temperance and women's rights in the 19th Century.

45. Hazel and Alice, record, Rounder 0027. Highly recommended record of traditional and feminist songs by Hazel Dickens and Alice Gerrard.

46. Hedy West, Volume Two, record, Vanguard VSD 9162. Traditional music.

47. Hillbilly Women, by Kathy Kahn. Garden City, N.Y.: 1973, Doubleday.

48. Honor Thy Womanself, record, Rounder 4006. Contemporary and traditional music by a chorus of women, with back up by Roaring Jelly, a country dance-type orchestra. Songs of Carolyn McDade sung by the Arlington Street Women's Caucus.

49. Hootenanny at Carneige Hall, record, Folkways FN2512.

50. Hootenanny Songbook. New York: Consolidated Music Publishers, 1963.

51. I Hate the Capitalist System, record, Paredon P--1014. Sung by Barbara Dane.

52. I Know You Know, Meg Christian album (and songbook) on Olivia. Order both from Olivia Records, Box 70237, Los Angeles, CA 90070.

53. Irish Folk Songs for Women, record, Folkways FG3518. Sung by Lori Holland. Traditional pining-away type songs.

54. Jimmy Rodgers Memorial Folio, Vol. I. New York: Peer International Corp. (1619 Broadway, NYC 10019), 1967.

55. Joan Baez in Concert, record, Part Two. Vanguard VSD 78113.

56. Joan Baez Songbook, New York: Ryerson Music Pub., 1964.

57. Lacemaking in the East Midlands, by Margaret Harner and Trefor Mitchell.

58. Lavender Jane Loves Women, record, Women's Wax Works, A001. Gay songs sung by Alix Dobkin, flute by Kay Gardner. Original and beautiful pop-classical music. (215 W. 92nd. St., NYC 10025)

59. Lovely on the Water, record, Topic 12TS216. Sung by Frankie Armstrong. Traditional English ballads with positive images of women.

60. Maid of Constant Sorrow, record, Elektra 7200. Sung by Judy Collins.

61. Malvina Reynolds Songbook, New York: Schroder Music (2207 Parker St., Berkeley, CA 94704).

62. Mooncircles, Kay Gardner album. Distributed by Olivia Records (no. 70).

63. Mountain Moving Day, record, Rounder 4001. Original feminist rock band music by the Chicago Women's Liberation Rock Band and the New Haven Women's Liberation Rock Band.

64. New City Songster, magazine, Vol. 7, January, 1972. A periodical of British folk music (35 Stanley Ave., Beckenham, Kent, BR3aPU).

65. New Lost City Ramblers and Cousin Emmy, record, Folkways 31018.

66. New Lost City Ramblers Songbook, ed. by Pete Seeger, John Cohen and Hally Wood. New York: Quick Fox, 1965.

67. The New Woman's Survival Sourcebook, a comprehensive catalog of womens' resources. A good section on women's music, women's presses, much more.

68. Nine to Five, newsletter. c/o YWCA, 140 Clarendon St., Boston, MA 02116.

69. Oh My Babe Blues, Vol. 2, 1924-28, record, Biograph 120ll. Sung by Ma Rainey.

70. Olivia Records, Box, 70237, Los Angeles, CA 90070 (213-389-4243). A feminist record company! They produce records (Meg Christian, Cris Williamson) and a songbook (Meg Christian), and distribute other records (Kay Gardner, High Risk). Write to them for a catalog, also for information on how to become an Olivia distributor in your area.

71. Ola Belle Reed, record, Rounder 0021. Traditional music.

72. Paid My Dues, magazine, Vol. I, No. 1 (Woman's Soul Pub. Co., P.O. Box 5476, Milwaukee, WI 53211. A quarterly women and music journal. Also have published booklet on producing concerts and a discography of women's music. Write to subscribe, or to submit material to the magazine.

73. Paid My Dues, Vol. 1, No. 2.

74. Pennsylvania Songs and Legends, by George Kornson. Baltimore: Johns Hopkins Press, 1949.

75. Pete Seeger at the Village Gate: Vol. 2, record, Folkways FA2451.

76. Pete Seeger: Three Saints, Three Sinners and Other People, record, Columbia Folk Odyssey, 32-16-0266.

77. Philo Records, Earth Audio, The Barn, N. Ferrisburg, VT. Rosalie Sorrels records with them now. She says they (unlike any other recording company) don't rip off the musicians. They do good quality work. Write for information on Rosalie's record and other artists, female and male.

78. Poor Pearl, Poor Girl, by Anne Cohen. Austin: University of Texas Press, 1973. American Folklore Memoir Series No. 58. The anatomy of one murder ballad in its variations and chronology.

79. Read 'Em and Weep, by Sigmund Spaeth. New York: Doubleday, Page and Co., 1927.

80. Ritchie Family of Kentucky, record, Folkways FA2316. Featuring Jean Ritchie.

81. Rounder Records, c/o Roundhouse, Box 474, Somerville, MA 02144. Rounder distributes the records of Hazel and Alice, The Arlington Street Women's Caucus, Holly Near, The Chicago and New Haven Women's Liberation Rock Bands, Malvina Reynolds, Barbara Dane, Aunt Molly Jackson, Sarah Ogan Gunning, Anne Romaine, Peggy Seeger, Frankie Armstrong, and songs of the suffragists. Send for catalog.

82. Sarah Ogan Gunning, record, Folk Legacy 26. Songs written and interpreted by Sarah Ogan Gunning.

83. Shake Sugaree: Elizabeth Cotten, Vol. 2, record, Folkways FTS31003.

84. Singing Family of the Cumberlands, by Jean Ritchie. New York: Oxford Press, 1955. The life story of

this fine ballad singer and some good insights into the place of women as balladeers integrating songs with life.

85. Sing Out! , magazine, November/December 1972. New York (106 W. 28th St., New York, NY 10001). Especially issues Jan/Feb '74, and Jan/Feb '71).

86. Song Fest, ed. by Dick and Beth Best. New York: Crown, 1966.

87. Songs and Stories of Aunt Molly Jackson, record, Folkways 5457. Sung by John Greenway.

88. Songs for Swinging Housemothers, ed. by Frank Lynn. Newcastle, NH: Chandler.

89. Songs of a Changing World, ed. by Jon Raven. London: Ginn & Co., 1972.

90. Songs of the Suffragettes, record, Folkways 5281.

91. Songs of Work and Freedom, ed. by Edith Fowke and Joe Glazer. Garden City, N.Y.: Dolphin, 1960.

92. The Art of the Jug Band, record, Prestige/Folklore (out of print). By the True Endeavor Jug Band.

93. The Liberated Woman's Songbook, ed. by Jerry Silverman. New York: Macmillan, 1971.

94. The Working Girl, record, Voyager 3055. Sung by Kathy Kahn. Good "working girl" songs from traditional sources.

95. Traveling Lady, record, Sire/Polydor SI5902. By Rosalie Sorrels.

96. Vermont Folksongs and Ballads, ed. by Flanders. Brattleboro: Stephen Daye Press, 1932.

97. Virgo Rising: The Once and Future Woman, record, Thunderbird 7030. (Thunderbird Records, 325 Flint St., Reno, Nevada) Contains traditional and contemporary feminist songs by Malvina Reynolds, Janet Smith, Meredith Tax, Charlies Aunts.

98. What, Woman, and Who, Myself, I Am, edited by Rosalie Sorrels, an anthology of songs and poetry of women's experience. Wooden Shoe, 1036 Solano Ave., Sonoma, CA 95476

99. Who Knows Where the Time Goes, record, Elektra 74033. By Judy Collins.

100. Witches and War Whoops, record, Folkways 5211. Collected and performed by John MacAllister. New England witch songs, fascinating and historically documented lyrics.

101. Woman Is My Name, songbook, by Lanayre Liggera. Boston: 1971 (out of print).

102. Women and Music, by Sophia Drinker. New York: Coward & McCann, 1948. An incredible book (like The First Sex by E. G. Davis, only about music) about the rise and fall of women in (mostly classical) music.

103. Women: A Journal of Liberation, Vol. 3, No. 2 on Women's Culture, write 3028 Greenmount Ave., Baltimore, MD 21218.

104. Women's Songbook, ed. by Judith Busch and Laura X. Albany, CA: 1971. (out of print) Project of Women's Oral Herstory Library, 2325 Oak St., Berkeley, CA 94708).

Other Resources
Magazines and Publications

Musica, order from Indy Allen, 1668A Great Highway, San Francisco, CA 94112. A newsletter about "the women in music and the music in women."

Paid My Dues, From Woman's Soul Publishing, Inc., PO Box 11646, Milwaukee, WI 53211. This feminist journal of women and music ("the first and only") has produced six issues covering nationwide happenings in women's music. A subscription is a must for anyone who wants to keep up on festivals, records, and tapes and research. These same people produced a discography of records by women, *My Sisters' Song,* (see record resources), and a valuable little pamphlet on producing concerts called, strangely enough, *Producing Concerts.*

Sing Out! The Folk Song Magazine, 595 Broadway, New York, N.Y. 10012. This bimonthly magazine usually includes some coverage of women in the folk world and has included some heated discussions of tampering with sexist material. Their August, 1976 issue is a special on women.

Records

For the most complete listing of records by women, send for *My Sisters' Song* from Women's Soul Publishing Company (see *Paid My Dues* above). They have an exhaustive list of records, and have conveniently placed a woman's symbol next to records which have special interest to feminists.

45's

The Common Woman (Nadine) and Degradation, performed by High Risk, produced by Sister Love Prod. and distributed by Olivia Records, PO Box 70237, Dept. NW, Los Angeles, CA 90070.

Lady sung by Meg Christian and *If It Weren't for the Music* sung by Cris Williamson, Olivia Records.

Sara Ellen's Homemade Records, Suite 1, 315 Brunswick Ave, Toronto, Canada M5R 221 (4 songs, 45 size, 33½ speed).

Song for Cheryl and Eve's Song sung by Eve Morris, ESM Productions, 2417 11th Ave. E., Seattle, WA 98102.

Long Playing

Always A Lady by Rosalie Sorrels, Philo Records, available through Rounder.

The Changer and the Changed by Cris Williamson, Olivia Records.

First Borne by the Buffalo Gals, an all-woman bluegrass band. Revonah Records, Dept. M, Box 217, Ferndale, NY 12734.

The Deadly Nightshade by The Deadly Nightshade, Phantom Records, BPL 1-0955, 1790 Broadway, New York, NY. This record includes some fantastic songs, such as "High Flyin' Woman" and "Mr. Big."

Full Count by Willie Tyson, Lima Bean Records, Inc., 217 12th St. S.E., Washington, D.C. 20003.

Gettin' On Country by Anne Romaine, Rounder 3009. Many contemporary and original songs about working women.

The Greatest Illusion by Joanna Cazden, Sister Sun Records, 413 E. Malden, Seattle, WA 98112.

Hazel and Alice by Alice Gerrard and Hazel Dickens, Rounder Records.

Holly Near: A Live Album by Holly Near, Redwood Records, 565 Doolin Canyon, Ukiah, CA 95482.

Honor Thy Womanself by The Arlington Street Women's Caucus, Rounder Records.

I Know You Know by Meg Christian, Olivia Records. Olivia's first LP album, includes "Ode to A Gym Teacher" and others. Also in cassette.

If I Could Be the Rain by Rosalie Sorrels, Folk Legacy No. 31. Available from Folk Legacy Records, Sharon, CT 06069.

Lavender Jane Loves Women by Alix Dobkin, Kay Gardner and Patches Attom, Women's Wax Works A001, 215 W. 92nd St., New York, NY 10025.

Leave The Breads A-Burning by The Arlington Street Women's Caucus, GYN 2-75-2, PO Box 297, Arlington, MA 02174. The caucus's second album.

Living With Lesbians by Alix Dobkin featuring the Lesbian Power Authority. A great new record of songs written by Alix of *Lavender Jane Loves Women* fame. Available from Project No. 1, Preston Hollow, NY 12469.

Living in the Trees by Lorraine and Rick Lee, Folk Legacy FS1 No. 31, Folk Legacy.

Loner by Indra Allen from Cell 16, 14A Eliot St., Cambridge, MA 02138.

Malvina Reynolds: Held Over by Malvina Reynolds, Cassandra CFS 3688. From Schroder Music Co., 2027 Parker St., Berkeley, CA 94704. Send for a complete list of Malvina's books and records.

Mountain Moving Day by the New Haven Women's Liberation Rock Band and the Chicago Women's Liberation Rock Band, Rounder Records.

Mooncircles by Kay Gardner on Urana Records, distributed by Olivia Records. Kay's mystical circular cyclical music is her most recent development in exploring woman's spiritual side in music. She is one fo the few women writing women's classical music and exploring what might be called women's forms in it.

Rounder Records c/o Roundhouse, Box 474, Somerville, MA 02144. Rounder distributes the records of Hazel and Alice, The Arlington Street Women's Caucus, Holly Near, The Chicago and New Haven Women's Liberation Rock Bands, Malvina Reynolds, Barbara Dane, Aunt Molly Jackson, Sarah Ogan Gunning, Anne Romaine, Peggy Seeger, Frankie Armstrong, and songs of the suffragists. Send for catalog.

Sing A Rainbow by Ginni Clemens, Folkways 7637 distributed by Rounder.

You'll Be Hearing More From Me by Jody Aleisan, Second Moon, 12347 17th St., NE, Seattle, WA 98125. Out of print and no longer available, but you could write for information.

Virgo Rising: The Once and Future Woman by Malvina Reynolds, Janet Smith, Meredith Tax, Charlies Aunts, Thunderbird Records, 1420 N. Virginia, Reno, NV 89503.

You Can Know All I Am by Holly Near, Redwood Records. Her latest album featuring "Flyin'," and "Sister, Woman, Sister."

Tapes

Casse Culver: Live in Concert by Casse Culver from Sweet Alliance Music, PO Box 2879, Washington, D.C. 20013.

Linda Shear/A Lesbian Portrait by Linda Shear from Old Lady Blue Jeans, c/o VWU 200 Main St., Northampton, MA 01060.

National Women's Music Festival Tapes The first (1974) festival features the Clinch Mountain Back Steppers, Casse Culver, Carolyn McDade, Nancy Ackerman, Vickie Randle, Dody Adkins, Meg Christian, Pamela Polland, Cris Williamson and others. The second (1975) features Terry Garthwaite and band, Vicki Randle, Suni Paz, Kristin Lems, Ginni Clemmens, Jeanne Mackey and Mary Trevor, The New Harmony Sisterhood Band, Bessie Burkes, Cathy Winter, Dee Werner, Carol Rowe and April Kassisier, Holly Tannen and the Boyer Vamily. Each from National Women's Music Festival, PO Box 2721, Station A, Champaign, IL 61820.

Songs of Struggle and Celebration by Jeanne Mackey and Mary Trevor featuring "Truck Drivin' Woman", "The Ones Who've Gone Before Us" and a booklet with words and chords. Order from Mary Trevor, 1629 Newton St. NW, Washington, D.C. 20010.

Songbooks

The Arlington Street Caucus Songbook compiled by The Arlington Street Women's Caucus. Boston: Arlington Street Women's Caucus, 1975. Available from PO Box 297, Arlington, MA 02174.

The Berkeley Women's Music Collective Songbook, words and music by The Berkeley Women's Music Collective. Write them at 2838 McGee, Berkeley, CA 94703.

Born A Woman by Rita MacNeil. Canadian Women's Educational Press, Suite 305, 280 Bloor St. W., Toronto, Ontario, Canada. 1974.

Curses & Songs & Poems by Lee Rudolph. Alice James Books, 1974, 138 Mt. Auburn St., Cambridge, MA 02138.

Growin' Songs by Patty Hale. c/o JEMF Inc., Folklore and Mythology Center, UCLA, Los Angeles, CA. 90024.

Hang In There Songbook by Holly Near, Jeff Langley and friends. Los Angeles: Peace Press, 1975. Redwood Records, 565 Doolin Canyon, Ukiah, CA 95482.

I Know You Know: A Songbook and Scrapbook of the Album by Meg Christian and friends. Available from Olivia Records.

The Malvina Reynolds Songbook by Malvina Records from Schroder Music Company.

Songs for the Liberated Woman by Polly Perkins. Published by Kahn & Averill, 25 Thurloe St., London.

Songs of Suffrage from Deliverance Press, 1032 Denner St., Kalamazoo, MI 49007.

Turned-On Woman Songbook by Ruth Mountaingrove. From New Woman Press, PO Box 56, Wolf Creek, OR 97497.

What, Woman, and Who, Myself, I Am edited by Rosalie Sorrels. An anthology of songs and poetry of women's experience. Available from Philo Records, Earth Audio, The Barn, N. Ferrisburg, VT.

Working Women's Music: Songs from the Textile and Garment Industries by Evelyn Alloy. New England Free Press, 6 Union Square, Somerville, MA 02143. (In Press)

Coming Out

A number of new albums are being produced as we go to press.

Be Be K'Roche, a latin, blues and rock band from the San Francisco Bay area is recording with Olivia Records.

Berkeley Women's Music Collective is producing their own record. Write them at 2838 McGee, Berkeley, CA 94703.

Deadly Nightshade is producing their own album on the Phantom label.

Hazel and Alice are recording with Rounder Records.

About the Editors

Joyce Cheney

Living in New England has taught me an appreciation for roots, for a heritage. I've been singing traditional songs; even though my life, opinions and options differ somewhat from those of women in traditional songs, they are my past. I want to know where we came from, in both a personal and a political sense.

I was trying to sing traditional songs and be a feminist at the same time. The songs I was singing supported role models I didn't want at all; it was hard to relate to some of the characters. I didn't want folks to have to listen to that stuff even one more time. I wanted to integrate two important factors of my life--feminism and music.

And then I came out. If you think it's hard finding good songs to sing as a feminist, try finding songs that a lesbian can relate to!

I started digging for feminist songs. At International Women's Day, March 14, 1974, I met Deborah and Marcia, and we began to work together on the songbook.

You can say things in a song that it is hard to say as strongly or intimately in speech, and because it's in a song, the message will stick longer. Song is a tool of change for any movement--for carrying messages, and for generating enthusiasm. And it's fun!

I'm part of a women and children's collective in Vermont. We're learning how to be family for each other.

Marcia Deihl

In 1970 I heard my first "women's music." It was a live concert at Boston University, with Bev Grant, feminist folksinger, and the New Haven Women's Liberation Rock Band. The theoretical significance of the event didn't concern me at the time--I was just elated at hearing, for the first time, the thoughts that had been raised in my C-R group put into a cultural form--especially music. I was majoring in music history at the time, but had gradually been disenchanted with the male-dominated, sterile and unprogressive atmosphere which accompanies the academic music history world. For two years after that concert, I couldn't enjoy listening to music of any kind anymore, let alone music with lyrics that had become insulting and irrelevant. Without any music that I could relate to, I had successfully turned off my emotions by my intellect's admonitions for more relevant music.

After two years of working as a secretary (still at Boston University) and puttering around as a general feminist politico in various groups, I saw a course being offered at the Cambridge-Goddard Graduate School for Social Change in the Feminist Studies Department--Women and Music! Hot damn! I took my hard-saved money and enrolled; the result, in part, is this book. We studied folklore, feminist theory and culture theory --trying to define a women's music. Luckily, we had access to Rounder Records of Somerville, a collective of people who have been sympathetic enough to feminist music to produce the *Mountain Moving Day* album, and to open their exhaustive collection of recorded traditional music to us. As well as reading and working on this songbook, the students in the course formed a women's band which is still alive and healthy today: The New Harmony Sisterhood Band. The songs that we dug up met with a great response from the Boston feminist community and we wanted to get them out to others. I was even able to (finally!) use my undergraduate skills in music in a practical way by copying, arranging and transcribing most of the music in this book.

What seemed like a nice little thing to do--play music in a feminist band--at one time now has turned into one of the most exciting phenomenons of our lives. We have watched as women's culture has grown from a few attempts to today's present mushrooming of books, songs, movies and plays. There is real emotional satisfaction in making women's music, but that is not all there is. It is important for me to realize that we are not simply entertainers, but that we are creating the strength for a movement that has the greatest potential for change this country has seen in decades. I am firmly convinced (yes, I have read political and economic theory, Mr. Leftist) that women's culture is revolutionary, and, best of all, it is accessible to large numbers of women. When we begin to see that it is not we ourselves who are wrong, but it is *they* who are controlling us, we take the first step toward the liberation of ourselves and of all such outsiders.

Deborah Silverstein

It's usually pretty easy for me to say what I have to say, but somehow this particular task is difficult and I've kept putting it off. Perhaps it's that there is something so final about describing yourself on paper--these words will always be here, long after my life has changed and no longer resembles this particular picture. I guess I do feel comfortable mentioning the things that seem to be constants in my life--throughout all the changes. It's very important to me to have a clear and realistic understanding of the world around me--and my relationship and responsibilities to it. It's important to me to share what I've come to understand with others, even when they'd rather not hear it. It's important to me that I continue to experience the joy, strength and pain of friendship, love, and struggle. AND, I love music and I love to sing! In many ways, all of these things have become part of what women's music has come to mean for me.

Publishing with Diana Press Expenses and Receipts

We thought it would be helpful, both to us and to our readers, to explain some of the process that resulted in Diana Press's publication of the songbook. After looking for over a year, two publishing prospects emerged within a week of each other--Diana Press and Moon Books-Random House. We were faced with the choice between a relatively small feminist press (Diana) and a feminist publishing house (Moon Books) affiliated with Random House's press and distribution network. The decision was not an easy one, but in the end we chose to have the book done by Diana. We've included here a letter which Deborah wrote to the women of Moon Books, explaining the issues that went into making that decision. We hope that you view this not as a choice between right and wrong, but as a choice between different paths which are, hopefully, extending toward common goals.

Since Diana does have a small (but growing) distribution network, we welcome the efforts of anyone who has the time, energy, and ideas to help broaden the distribution of *All Our Lives* to as many people as possible.

December 7, 1975

Dear Ani and Kent,

I kept putting this letter off, but I've wanted to write and personally thank you for the work you did, the last letter you wrote, and apologize for the struggles that we put you through. Making the Moon vs. Diana Decision was one of the most difficult I have ever faced, in that I feel my decision will have effects that extend far beyond me personally.

I think there were a few major factors operating in my and/or our decision. First was, would Diana be able to carry it off, that is, produce a comparably good book? After talking with them, we felt assured that they could. Second, and in my opinion, the most controversial issue, is distribution. There's obviously no comparison between Diana's and Random House's network. It is likely or certain that more non-movement women would have access to the book were it distributed by Random House--and there are certain undeniable advantages to having your information distributed among the masses. The conflict is in having a major corporation profit from this venture. I don't think there is a clear answer. Your decision to work with or use Random House does not "smack of revisionism" to us as strongly as you might suspect. But I know you must not need me to tell you that you will be free to use Random House only so long as Random House chooses to use you. To some extent, I think that it's an indication of how non-threatening the radical (women's or otherwise) movements still are to the corporate powers. They're willing to market whatever

199

will sell so long as there's no danger of their products turning around and taking control over them.

The other side of this distribution issue is that if the book does prove to be a viable commodity, it will strengthen Diana's distribution both within and beyond the women's community. This would give me more satisfaction than strengthening Random House's contacts in the women's community.

Another issue I know I had to deal with was what it felt like to say no to having a book done by Moon—Random House. Never before has such a 'prestigious' American carrot been dangled in front of my nose. There was a lot of ego that went into saying, "Random House wants to do our book." It has been an unforgettable lesson in what it can mean to presume to say "I am engaged in a struggle against an oppressive capitalist, imperialist government." The weapons of the state often appear in the guise of gifts.

A final idea that I thought and talked about is that in a certain sense, I don't consider this book 'mine or ours' because most of the book exists due to the energy, struggles, and creativity of many other women. If this book belongs to anyone, it belongs to the women's movement and all the other struggles for liberation that gave rise to the songs in the book. I feel it's important that I remember that it is other people's pain and triumphs that we are putting to use. In this sense, it is the movement that made this book possible, and the movement should benefit and grow as much as possible from whatever this book has to offer.

So these are some of the thoughts and feelings that went into the decision in my heart and head. I want to thank you once again for your letter. I hope that if I'm in a position similar to yours at some time, I'll be able to respond with as much encouragement.

Sincerely,

Budget for Songbook for first 5,000 copies

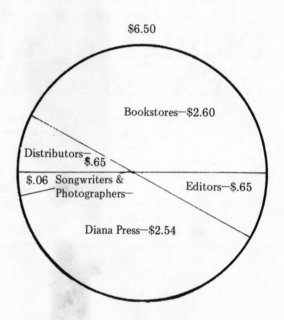

Editor's Expenses
Photo-copying, mailing, phone 884.00

Production Expenses
Cover design 130.00
Typesetting 560.00
Note calligraphy 497.00
Paste-up 210.00
Camera work 500.00
Printing text 3,750.00
Printing cover 150.00
Text Paper 1,878.00
Cover Paper 160.00
Cover lamination 250.00
Collating 500.00
Perfect Binding 500.00

Royalties
Photographers 470.00
Song Writers 745.00
Editors (10% of 4,500 sales) 2,925.00
.... 14,609.00

Receipts from Sales

The books will be sold at a retail price of $6.50. Forty per cent of that price goes to bookstores, women's bookstores primarily. In addition, another 10% goes to the distributors, Women in Distribution primarily. Therefore, we make 50% of the retail price of the book. From a first run of 5,000 copies we expect to sell 4,500. The other 500 will be sent out as review copies, free copies to the editors, complimentary copies to the songwriters, photographers, etc. At $3.25 each 4,500 sold copies will bring in $14,625.00.

Projected receipts 14,625.00

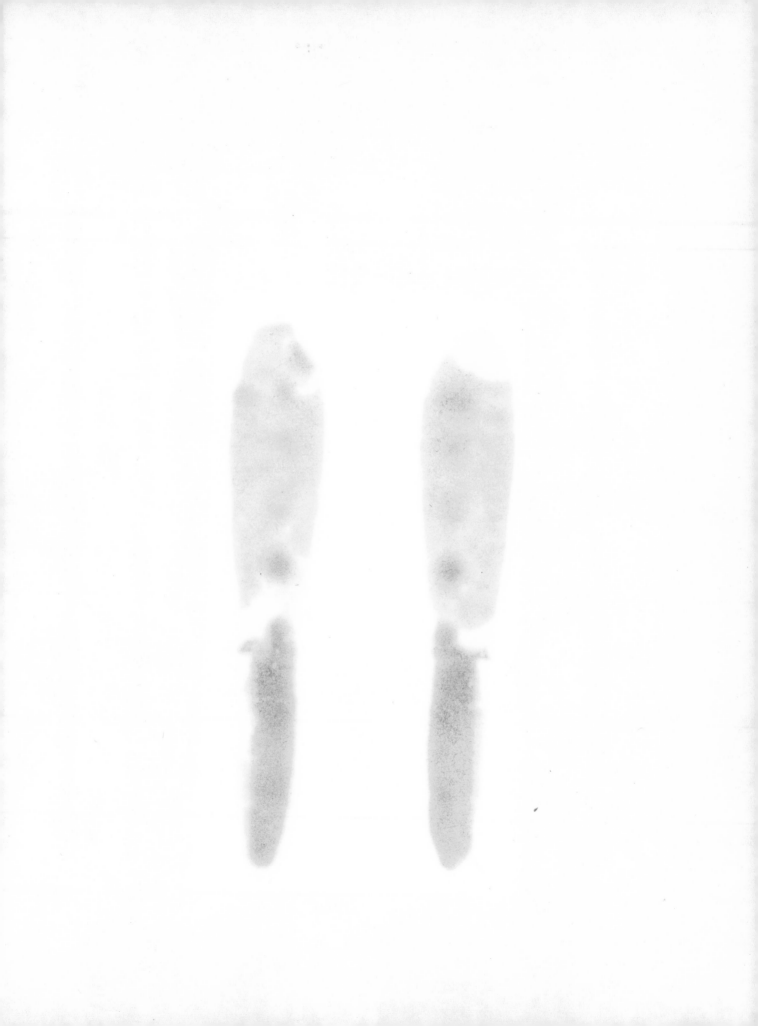

DATE DUE

GAYLORD   PRINTED IN U.S.A.